Y0-BED-372

A FLOWER FOR SIGN

THE MACMILLAN COMPANY
NEW YORK · BOSTON · CHICAGO · DALLAS
ATLANTA · SAN FRANCISCO

MACMILLAN & CO., LIMITED
LONDON · BOMBAY · CALCUTTA
MELBOURNE

THE MACMILLAN COMPANY
OF CANADA, LIMITED
TORONTO

A FLOWER FOR SIGN

By

LOUIS STANCOURT

NEW YORK

THE MACMILLAN COMPANY

1937

Set up and printed. Published February, 1937.

FIRST PRINTING.

PRINTED IN THE UNITED STATES OF AMERICA
BY THE STRATFORD PRESS, INC., NEW YORK

FOREWORD

I HAVE been asked to make it plain at once, that the account herewith set forth is that of my own life. I wish, sincerely wish, I could say it were not. Looking back, I see myself and am stunned. It is a fight still, but I have said I will go on, and go on even though flung down on my back again. The adversary is myself; you know the same adversary. Across the dark, Man-in-the-Street, I give you my hand. Since birth, each of us has been fighting to get through. But when I tried to run up your back to get ahead of you, I did not know you. If Caesar orders us both to war, and each of us on opposing sides, we know we must cross swords and lunge or be lunged at. You may be white, and I black, or you yellow, I brown; but the steel through us would find the agony of the one exactly like the other's. We are one man, of one experience, one birth and death beginning and ending our little course on earth. For the moment I hail that one man, and beg the One Whom I now understand for our Father, "Please get us through."

THE AUTHOR

Roosevelt, L. I.
Feast of Holy Name of Mary
Sept. 12, 1936.

CONTENTS

BOOK ONE

Chapter I

AS IT WAS IN THE BEGINNING

The life of this man whom we will call Joseph is not important. But the road he made may guide others of us passing through. It seems less a life than a continuity, for an instant revealed by a flash in the dark. We see a man, and a road, a wall, and a soul trying to get over, and self flinging him back. Mostly, a picture of a man flung down on his back again . . . and of one last piercing cry of discouragement, protest and aloneness, the benighted cry, wanting mother to find him in the dark. And of a wall suddenly dynamited.

We will try to go back to the beginning, while the last echo of the blast of deliverance dies in the night.

The Tireds, Joseph's family, lived in a street of the parish of Our Lady of Loreto, in East New York, Brooklyn. Joseph remembers a sagging wooden tenement, in which the family flat was on the second or third floor; and always another pig-tailed sister or brother coming along to tremble under the fearful frown of the father. He also recalls the gnarled old Sicilian sing-songing his sidewalk wares: "Who eats, eats"; the tall lank neighbor with pirate beak and brass ear-rings and yet the most gentle nature he ever knew; the dapper stranger who dashed out of a shop with cheek opened from temple to chin, to scream and roll over in the gutter; the undertaker's window past whose coffin he would fearfully run; the marble face of his little brother, nose up in the peace of the death-box; the collapse of the new church wall upon seven men, and the wailings; the piece of cornbread with the blood from his sister's face upon it, when he had pushed her down the steps for not giving him some; the night's terror, barricaded in the kitchen where the father stood grimly waiting with an ax, because three whom he had discharged from the street-railroad were out to stiletto him; and placid Uncle-the-Archangel waiting in the dark by the rear fire-escape, with a baseball bat; and the gentle-faced girl-mother hovering troubled in the kitchen in her night dress to which the two boys clung; and the father abruptly getting up to burst out, "And must I huddle in my house like a caught rat?" In his fearful calmness he ripped the barricade away and flung open the door to flood the hall with lamplight, into which he called: "Who comes, let him come, the door is open." With dignity he looked from it, turned, shut it and bade, "Noh, to bed, it nears midnight."

And the festa!

The festa is no more, but Joseph sees it as it was, with its great concourse of people, its far-murmuring gaiety, the lights strung across the streets, and the dazzling sweetness of the Madonna looking down on her children.

The preparations took many days. First the vanguard would bustle along, all brisk and important, putting up tall painted poles down each side of the street at hundred-foot intervals. And the people would joyously call, one to the other, "*La festa, la festa vene!*" The festa was coming.

How the advance army bustled! And how patiently. There were endless great boxes full of tumbler-size glasses, all colored green, red, yellow, and the shades between, that were destined to be set in the pattern of wire to be arched over the street. The glasses were to be filled with oil and a wick; the tremendous labor can be imagined when the number of glasses in each arch is considered.

But when the vari-colored glasses were lighted— There is nothing soft enough to describe the muted brilliance of night over the archway of glasses, all blending, a splash of glowing gold, green and flame, with the soft goldenness of the Virgin toning it down, casting a violet diffusion throughout. Somehow it was like the Madonna's robe—violet and sun. Hope on twilight. Or stars on fading sky, flashed by the sun.

The later electric-bulb archways do not seem to catch this blend. They make a sharp muddle, where gentle diffusion is needed. A Mardi Gras is suggested, not the coming of a mother-queen.

Madonna was the heart of the festa. The festa might be in honor of this saint or that, but her spirit imbued it. And because of this, no labor to the Italian heart was labor. Hence the seeming over-emphasis on preparations and theatre.

Following the archway-men, came the favored people who were to command the sidewalk festa-stands of foodstuffs. They jabbered and fussed, scolded and shrugged, and went on mounting their stands, deaf to the remarks of others who had failed to get the favor of a spot—and the certainty of abundant sales. The stand was simple. Two end boxes that were also store-bins, or barrels with boards across. A crosspiece would be erected overhead from short poles or boards.

Over the cross-piece would be strung festoons of roasted nuts and figs. The process would leisurely consume most of a week; then suddenly the stands would blossom out with colored paper coverings, and by this sign the day before the festa had come.

The last preparations grew up about the grandstand where the band concerts were to be. Here an elaborate pine-board bandstand would leisurely sprawl out, climb up, cross over to shrug a floor up, and suddenly it was ready for the decorations and the glass-light display. Underneath it the sidewalk people would pass in a moment's darkness, and boys would trustfully hover, feeling the wood and the bright cloths, gladdening at the infallible sign of another great day come true. Among them, lingering confidently, would be Joseph, his face saying to each adult passing underneath, "She'll be here soon."

To him "she" was God; he knew no God other than the awesome sweetness that seemed so far above, and so abidingly near in everything;—even when he hid under the bed lest something he had done should find him out, he knew Madonna was marking it reproachfully in the book. For Madonna saw all things and read thoughts; there was no hiding. There was a great painting down on the church wall by the pew-ends; flames towered and roared there, and people scantily robed begged uselessly over clasped hands for another chance. . . . Joseph huddled back within himself from the awful everlastingness of it all, with delicious thrills of highly imaginative anguish, as if tempted to see how quickly those flames should lick him, and spring away, yet with great faith in the protectiveness of Madonna, who would keep him from being thrust into the flames, like a mother imperturbably sitting down to peel vegetables with an eye on him. But sometimes he remembers it as a postcard, not a wall.

This was Joseph's childhood picture. Looking back now, he inclines to think it was a postcard view, which in dozy Sunday memories he envisioned across a church wall. There were always such postcards in his mother's house, by the glass Crucifix.

The Crucifix was a massive cross some ten inches high, of a milky glass resembling marble. Jesus drooped wearily from it, through all his childhood, without ever once suggesting any meaning to him. It stood a little insecurely on his mother's mantelpiece by reason of a piece chipped out of the cupped bottom-rest; yet never once was it known to fall over.

Here is a description of "festa-going," as sketched by Joseph in one of more than one hundred previous attempts to report his life:

"At last, her best dress on over underskirts, and her gentle face transported like any girl's, she would stand by while my father wandered about the flat with his deepset frown, making up his mind whether to let her go or not, while she pretended not to care, with a rub of an itch on her elbow or a pat of her burnished top-knot of hair, a rub of a blouse button, and her long-cornered eyes ever stealing a dismayed glance to see this slow man making up his mind. But suddenly clearing his throat he would announce, like a relenting Caesar, 'Noh—and see that you waste no more than two hours or I'll let you see a head flying off with a slap.' And as he turned away she would quickly take my hand, urging, 'Fly—! before he repents that he permitted—' And down the halls we would scuttle, breathless and giggling at such haste—because he had been known to hold her up with a command, 'O, Assú—!' and send her to go to the store for him first, or to cook him something.

"Hand in hand we would be drawn quickly to the lighted concourse, by the spirit of the festa, and I would resent every old fishwife of either sex who must stop to ramble through a solemn chat, when they ought to see that I was taking her out to laugh and be glad for two hours.

"And the glowing dead-end of the archway would hail us afar, urging us to hurry through the desert, and suddenly we were sucked into the exciting blur of light, bodies, voices, movement, and glimpses of busy stands, a drum signal—and Sousa's Stars and Stripes Forever! Festa bands are catholic.

"Down the gutter, after the band had strolled round the corner, we would shuffle with the packed multitude, keyed to every laugh and sound and smell, every blend of glowing light, and never noticing the press of slow bodies. My senses were mostly riveted on the stands, their smell of nuts and sweetstuffs absolutely a heaven to me; they made my heart ache to go poaching a bit, with elaborate care and a darting hand; but my mother was so dismayed at such a business . . . and of late it had grown less and less in favor in Madonna's eyes.

"The stands would call me with their strings of roasted chestnuts, shelled or unshelled, and nuts and dried figs; another stand would be a whole tumbled gray sea of salted seeds, and roasted pea-beans, made more interesting by the generous sprinkling of white sand in which they had been crisped on an oven floor; there were no end of cakes and cookies, some as big as a hand and about as easily broken, but delightful to mull over in the mouth, till reduced enough to bite on suddenly—for which employment the Designer gave Italians strong teeth. The smaller cakes had added toughness to make up for small size, so that the common complaint, with an accusing stare over bristling moustaches, would be, 'And what: must you bring out these same cakes year after year, till sold?' And the reply would be savage. But hardest to resist was a creamy tough candy, shot through with nuts, and tending to pink, whose composition remains a mystery; my father declared it the highest art of the plasterers—and if in rummaging through the bags we brought home he failed to find a block of *torroni* big enough, we should both hear of it.

"Suddenly within the jam of people would come merrily sing-songed through the nose, '*A pizza—aaá pizza; ú pizzaro!*' The pie-man! How we would all open up a lane, making way for the merry Neapolitan, who would scuttle down among us, balancing his huge tray high, and selling out before a hundred feet were covered. His wares were huge discs of hot soft bread-dough, covered with melted grated cheese and tomato sauce, deceivingly docile and highly rubberized, but eagerly pounced upon. Mother would be sure to stand dancing till she had one in her wary fingers like a hot potato —and we would both pull, and stuff, and choke, giggling.

"Then we would go on a mild buying spree, sampling frugally of nuts, beans and cookies, to wash it all down with a drink of anybody's idea of lemonade. And for the time appeased, we would seek the spirit of the festa.

"We always found it. Everywhere the brightsome sprite would bid us look and laugh, and forget yesterday, and live. At a spaghetti house's sidewalk stand I saw an American under a tilted straw-hat, eating spaghetti in our manner with his hands, and laughing at the shrugging back of his lady who would not dip into our festa gaiety; and our people pausing to regard him with neighborly favor for thus honoring us. Moving leisurely down wherever the pack of bodies willed, we would take in glimpses in passing: the fiercely moustached balloon man, forever turning sharply around to glower in search of some guilty face, when pins burst his wares; a stray massive policeman, red-faced and wooden under his pot-helmet, drifting majestically down among us; a bevy of girls with elbows hooked together, laughing and breasting a counter-sea, to gasp amid sudden handfuls of confetti; ox-like young men with garters around arms and roses over ears, cheerily looking for romance; someone's girlie, bawling 'Ma-a!' at every step, and digging her eyes out with a grubby fist while polite men squatted down to ask where she lived; an important man behind a nut stand, turning with incredible speed to whack his stick down across a poacher's knuckles, and then sing out languidly, '*Chicheri é simienti—passatiempo!*' Beans and seeds, pass time; a nickel's worth would last hours, nibbling them out of the pocket, strolling. I would see, rarely, someone's dour uncle, rambling in all directions in his wine, muttering to himself, to walk sharply into a stout woman's face, perhaps, and be pushed four people away. Once I saw a man grasp the wrist of a hand slipping into his coat pocket; but all that came of it, to my breathless disappointment, was a stiff, 'Wey, wey, wey—what does this signify?' with a bristling stare at an apologizer moving calmly away. It is hard to get up a fight in a festa.

"But how simple the gladness of my mother! I have that,

and nobody can take it from me; she had accepted me from the start, seeing that I understood everything in her; it warms me gently still. She was free to live joyfully in the festa, and she lived, laughing at everything,—darting down to rescue her cakes and nuts from shuffling feet, with great peril to the fingers, to get up ruefully and wander down with the stragglers . . . and somewhere suddenly the wonder for which we had come would happen.

"She would stand stock still, transported with wonder, her long-fringed eyes flung wide to it, lips parting. 'Look—la Madonna!' And there in the sudden lane in the street where the parade shuffled, shouldered high across poles on a throne, all golden and creamy and blue, would be the Presence that filled all my childhood with a mother-love.

"And with a flushed and infinitely tender confusion my mother would go through the people to pin a dollar out of our scantiness on the violet skirt, as humble men lowered the throne to her.

"And seeing I understood."

With such an image to move him, he should have gone far. And yet he grew up an atheist.

His mother says gently to this, "Arcangelo." This was her brother. But his heart rebels at this explanation; the bristling, roaring being, strutting hugely behind a florid moustache and the deepest laughter Joseph ever heard, fills all childhood with gladness. For he told droll tales when the kitchen lamp was lit and the house abed. One night he interrupted them with the frantic sweep of a broom and a great cluttering noise after a sudden mouse on the floor, and lay down to roll over holding his sides lest he burst with peals of laughter. . . . Then in the door Father presented his fearful frown under his steepled bedcap, so that even the Archangel shuffled uneasily in his chair. "Noh, for a stable of neighing falling horses I looked. What transports itself here?"

"Nothing, Francí," meekly said stout Uncle.

"Thus was my thought."

But the Archangel had no use for God.

"*Domino beesk!*" he would solemnly intone, like the priest of the great paunch. "*Dong ee-dongle-ong—dong ee-dong!* 'Come, all the faithfuls, bring the money for the wine casks. *Ho, domino bees-ko o, oho, o!*' Ho, ho, ho, ho!" he would merrily laugh, pleased with his imitation. It was then that Joseph distrusted him, and loved him uneasily less. There was scarce room for Madonna where "Uncle Bill" was.

Joseph and his brother the first-born, after a few uneasy weeks of catechism class, where one met with hard lessons concerning an Authority called God, were rewarded with a postcard likeness of the Pope, which instantly was pasted on the bedroom wall. This was a personal triumph, for the priest, touring the basement classes, had scowled them down for laggards who could not understand the Oneness, God, in three parts. The postcard was such a sudden compliment on a brisk lesson, that Joseph thought it Madonna's defense of the brothers. Consequently, on the wall went the Pope, object of proud gazes. "You were both so happy, so full of the picture," the mother reminds Joseph, who had forgotten the incident.

Uncle Archangel shared the boys' bedroom. When he came from work, Joseph proudly pointed. "Look!—the present!" The beaming moon face rapidly contracted. "The Pope—; in my room!" Crash! went his ham fist through Pope and plaster.

"There was a fight—oo, the crash of it," unwillingly reports the mother. "Your father was protesting not the picture, but God, attacked by my brother. You hid under the bed while the fight rolled and clamored."

Joseph grew to boyhood, losing the image of the Madonna who had been very real . . . and now was like mists melting. Out of the last of them rose three boys on a box in the sun, inspecting themselves. "This is how babies come." Joseph slowly felt resentment. "They come in the midwife's bag; they cost mothers money; I cost ten dollars." They jeered. "Look—! He believes that stuff. Heh-hhh!" He went home passionately crying. The ache lasted days. At twelve years he lost a precious glow, a trustful belief. At twelve childhood died.

CHAPTER II

THE IMAGE MAKER

BOYHOOD was an odd evolution, lost in tender mist. It was a period of image-forming, born of rebellious tears over the discovery that childhood's abiding faith was based on myths. He needed an image to guide him, something to fill the world within, whose glow would also shine on the world without, and make it an indivisible part of the inner world in which he lived.

And people kept smashing it down, revealing things which he did not want, did not need . . . and rebelliously resisted; for they took from him all that was precious and abiding and real, that was intangibly part of himself: his vision.

Simultaneously with the discovery of the repulsive origin of babies, tumbled the chubby cherry image of Santa Claus, completely dissolving the wonder of Madonna, whose sweet face was no more. And now there was nothing. And he cried a long time in this barrenness.

He suddenly resented people. People, parents included, were strangers who said, "Toh!" and who dismissed the world of children, with an elaborateness that made one wander about, crying with desolation. They put you on their laps and said importantly, "Look—! it's this way." But reality had revealed itself behind a back-lot fence.

Life became a growing awareness of sensations, never resolved, ever full of wonder, ever urgently calling. But when he experimented with his discovered self they slapped his face violently. Then when he wanted to know why this was they slapped him again, and sent him to see if the newspaper had come, in a sharp silence. But the sweet sweep of urges once awakened grew a lingering consciousness, ever urging.

In the interlude of mist between childhood and boyhood, there burst a sudden horde of beings, some by way of fireside tales, some leaping from sandlot and gutter where boyhood hears creepy accounts of the world of darkness. And Joseph grew aware of a fearful dark, peopled with spirits, ghosts, black magic, dead bodies that waylay people, and hysteria-causing *scatzamaurielli*, dwarfed and fiendish, who were about a foot tall in red hose and steeple caps, and who danced and shrieked about the foot of the bed till parents ran up at once in the dark to thrust the lamp over the bed with a great tenseness. . . . After this to quiet his fears they would be with him till sleep came again.

Intermingled with these accounts were tales of old Italy, peopled with less fearsome spirits, that were sometimes the droll and beautiful tales which Joseph loved so. And they were all the more rare because they brought to the winter evening stove another father, a father without the grim frown that lashed with a clothesline whip, a father cheerily plucking a Toscano stogie to and from his story-telling grin.

Sometimes they were sudden bits of the wonder that had been Madonna . . . all the sweeter for refusing to come out quite *real*. For they suggested a world beyond broken faith's belief. These tales were of Paradiso. Paradiso, one learned, was a sunburst above the sky. The very good were taken up there—'way up high above the clouds, where no cold was, no stiletto-men, no pain, no terrifying frowns, no beatings. Only gladness was there. Dio was up there, that was why. Dio was surrounded with angels, who flew about with great beautiful wings, and came down to fetch the very good. All the others would be roasted in another place which Joseph had bitterly discarded as a fraud. He longed to accept Paradiso, but it was mentioned in the same breath with l'Inferno, which did not exist. There was no underground region where people burned in perpetual flames without ever getting burned up. Joseph knew that. There was only one being prowling about under the ground, and that was the Devil, when he was not dashing up on earth to snatch someone and thrust him into his private fire.

Joseph knew this terrifying being. He was very real. He had confronted Joseph suddenly, face-to-face in dreams. He had cloven hoofs, a burnt black body, a frightful grin, a spiked tail, and a huge pitchfork with which to spit you up and thrust you into the fire with a splitting laugh. The dangerous hour was the stroke of midnight; then he would suddenly swoop; he was bound to get someone, somewhere.

At that hour, said the knowing big-nosed stranger who told the boys, you could test your courage, and at the same time enrage the Devil. Just go down into the cellar with a bleeding red mass of beef and a knife, when midnight was nearing, never minding the darkness. Then at the precise stroke of the Devil's hour, stick the meat with the knife and call out abruptly, "Devil, Devil, Devil, catch me if you can!" But your mother help you, said the stranger, if you don't get up those stairs *without half a second lost*. People were known to be dragged back by the heel for missing the doorknob in the first grab.

And thenceforth Joseph in terror fled up or down the night hall past that cellar door . . . first casually whistling as he neared, to show his unconcern. And he had a fear of the dark, that was ever ready to verge on hysteria.

Then suddenly one night the Devil waylaid him.

It was the god-feast called *Carnivalo*. It is given each February to the ancient god of the harvest, by descendants of Rome all over the world. Its keynote is gaiety over a full table, behind jolly masks.

Upstairs, from the frowning father down to the newest Pigtail, they had their masks on, waiting till Joseph should come up the hall with the can of beer from the saloon. He too had his mask on . . . and perhaps the ancient god, thus honored, had enraged the Devil. For Joseph, coming fearfully on the run up the stairs past that cellar door, grew somehow aware of a *leap* gathering force behind, and of the mounting clatter of hoofs—and of a swift darkness plunging up past him along the wall to cut him off, a towering, expanding, leering shadow with fingers clutching. And screaming, Joseph swung the beer can at the black Thing sweeping the wall . . . and came to on the kitchen floor amid his stunned family, with the echo of hysteria singing in his ears.

"From henceforth," burst the troubled father of them all, "let no mouth breathe of devils in this house. For things that are not, are written in the mind, and truth goes unbelieved."

And he told no more ghost stories. And revolting, a dreamer, who could never believe, again swept out all his inner world of flitting beings.

But after this purging, the world was dispeopled. The dawn of boyhood was a period of stillness under a dead sun, in which people did chores and children arithmetic. There was no image to lighten it. And Joseph without an image, around which to build, was mechanical.

Heaven or Paradiso promised the last possibility. He suddenly turned his thoughts to this idea. If he could so much as only half see it, he could with some contrivance make something out of the angels, inventing secret missions for them, with this Dio the chief general of them, and Joseph thinking out the errands. It would be better than nothing. A world of merely playmates and people was unbearable.

But it was understood that Dom was up there, and somehow he could not imagine it around *him*.

Dom was dead. It had happened some ages before. Bundling the child up because he was just convalescing from pneumonia, also because he was a father's pet, referred to as "The Boy Italian," Joseph set him on a stone and went about recruiting some robbers for Cops and Robbers. Whenever Dom wailed, Joseph quit being the robbers' chief long enough to pick up the lollypop from the dirt or gather up the child who had fallen off the stone. He brought the bundled burden up from the winter sun, with a tired small grin looking out of a fiery countenance. Three days later Dom was nose-up and marble on the table, amid white darkness and tired sobs. There was a concourse around the parlor walls the last day, all the neighbors crying, while the first-born Nickey sat with a book and a cigar box at the kitchen table, entering in the book the name and into the cigar box the amount contributed by each neighbor coming to partake of the funeral. Father sat with his weary frown in the parlor, heavy-shouldered in his Sunday suit and bow tie. The undertaker, after some doubt, went briskly about the business of screwing the cover down where Dom looked up with stilled shininess and shut eyes; but startled out of his fixed stare, the father jumped up and pushed the man staggering away. "But can't I do this, who lifted him borning from his mother?" Screwing the lid down, tears whipped across his small hard brown eyes, so that he poorly found the screws. Then turning around, he looked about at them all, in the old dignity of moments when he had prepared to make a speech, and they sat duly waiting for it to begin, but he said in the sorrowing hush, "This is the Boy Italian." Then looking at them in great doubt the tears dashed his eyes again, and he sat and took his head in his hands, with sobs blocking his throat, the first and last time he was ever thus seen. And Joseph who had stood in dread of being charged with failing to guard Dom from catching his death, burst into tears.

Full of his debate over Heaven, now wanting it and now wanting it not, Joseph longed to get information. Caught suddenly and questioned, Father could be direct and exact. For he was a just father.

Joseph circled slowly around the room, making up the question warily, and was all at once standing before the frown which lifted up behind silver spectacles from the *Progresso Italo-Americano*'s spread of news events. "Noh?"

"Tell me about Paradiso—" all in a rush.

"Toh!" The burnt-brick face was surprisedly pleased. The paper went across the lap. "That place so uninteresting to a little *barongino*?" He must feel his little pleasure in teasing. "But who wants to hear of such foolish places?"

"But is it real?"

"Toh!" Then, putting aside the lightness, he was as Joseph liked him, absorbed in the question in hand.

"Heaven," he slowly said, piecing it out from his vision, "is a country up high—so high up that nobody of himself can reach it. But who can reach Heaven?" he looked up to ask, sober enough. "It is God Himself. And we, called back by distractions all the way. . . . Noh, it can be reached," he advised after some thought. "But do as God would have you, and He will show you."

"But what *is* Heaven?—make me see it," urged Joseph.

"Toh!" gently. "Then I am some ambassador, appointed to open a hole and show it? . . . But seek in the church," he said, simply, "and your heart will find it."

"They say, 'Be good; who made the world? God made the world; who is God? God is the creator of—of everything; who—' "

"But, questions are instruction, from which to ask more questions, surely. Know your heart, and ask. Then, what is Heaven, noh? Noh, Heaven is—but there is nothing down here to make a likening. A city where God is. It is everywhere, but it is located above all things. We look at the sky and see it up there. But it is God Himself. Then only draw on God Who then will draw you; and Heaven is the continuation of that, without the interference of this world."

Joseph said dubiously, "Oh."

The father gently patted his shoulder. "May it grow on you . . . Look again: God is obedience to authority. So, God is mother and father and priest, and the law of the land. God is doing just. God is growing straight and clean, and facing the wind. Noh, God is doing right, all that is right is God who put it in the heart. But Heaven is the reward for obeying the law of God: be just, help your neighbor and the stranger, do the duty before you, resist the bad; and failing, try again. Then Heaven," troubled for a word for it, "is the heart, seeking God who sent you. And finding Him is the joy of union again, never to die any more."

It registered in labored phrases. It came so instantly from conviction that Joseph longed to find a corner to grasp; it *felt* good. But he needed reality to identify it, as one feels a ledge of rock to sit on, a banana to eat—some outline in the sun. If only he could identify it by something—that it was wet, or round, or hot. He knew that he *wanted* to be drawn, but lacked knowing just *what* to be drawn to.

Then a thought occurred. Dominick. If a dead child could live there—; here was a corner to grasp.

"Dom is there? You said so."

"But Domí is there, securely," with much gentleness. "He went straight to God, for being without blame."

"He is happy there? You said so."

"But to be with God is happiness such as no man can feel. It is the great comfort, the peace supreme."

"Then you are very glad?"

"That your brother went there."

"Then why did you cry so?"

"But ghost of your father and your mother and who created you!" burst the father, startling the son away.

Joseph repeopled his world from books. The school of the Americans was full of promising images. These images shone with bright armor, and ran headlong after infidel princes whose armies had fallen. They were swordsmen for whatever was true and beautiful; and putting backs to rocks, they swung bravely against desperate odds, and, beaten, went slowly down; and suddenly shouting, white avengers dashed up, rescuing the torn-robed, white-faced image of the true whom the foe had felled. But at first Joseph ran weeping away and the idea was slow in growing . . . fruiting only after the year twelve had passed.

The swordsmen really began, perhaps, in the protective glow of Madonna, when the world was all awareness of a mother,—a mother who suddenly took him to a place of strangers and sharp-edged foreign speech, a place of sobbing rows called "School."

Joseph's loneliness was because this was the first time he was torn away from the hand of his mother, who seemed to *want* to leave him there in such strangeness. . . . But escaping from the rows of prison-children and finding a door to the instantly familiar sun, he walked straight into its face, till the tangle of streets was one with his sobs and tired legs, and he sat wearily down on a gutter curb. A lady with a baby carriage and a far suggestion of Madonna bent down to say sweet unknowable things and finally to give him cakes out of her carriage. Then going away she returned, pushing her carriage again, and a towering policeman rolled along beside her on a bicycle. And, pointing to Joseph crying wearily there, she went away while the policeman bent low to make rough kind demands in the same unknowable tongue. At the school they had queried him likewise, and making him stick out his tongue, with impatience they had examined it.

So now in answer to the queries he stuck out his tongue and waited till the policeman should examine it. But, instead, the blue giant abruptly put him astride his handlebars and rode him languidly in the sun . . . till he woke up in a dull damp dungeon past which police flitted. From somewhere came shambling a small ogre blinking behind a thick droop of moustache; he was so instantly one of Joseph's own world that the boy blurted out at once:

"I want my mother to find me," and jolted with sobs.

The ogre put his pushbroom against the wall and took off his visor cap to scratch his head with puzzled blinks. He said, "She has to go to the store first. What street are you from?" But Joseph was too desolate to answer.

Then the man distastefully said, "Hooh! Your father's name is Pauluzzo, he works on the garbage wagon."

Hotly denying this Joseph declared, "It is not, it is not! his name is Francí and he is boss of tracks in the street and the bad ones call him Charlie Hart."

"Oh—Charliardo! The Commandanto of Pacific Street." He came again and set Joseph on the table with peanuts to eat, till he finished sweeping the floor.

Then his mother burst wildly in; but seeing him calmly eating out of the bag she came with her old sweet smile.

"Look—! Peanuts." And they shared some . . . as when the festa had beckoned.

School suggested nothing. But suddenly he found an image evolved in the mists where Madonna and his mother had faded . . . and it came out a feeling for all who were like them both. And it was womanhood.

It was a blend of two widely separated forces. One was from the tender wonder awakened first behind that sand-lot fence. Wreathing mists gradually formed around the wonder; as he emerged from childhood this nebula took form and resolved itself, as in a dream, into a motherly woman, softly rounded in a winding sheet and smiling down with arms out, to warm him in her bosom. And he grew uneasily conscious of self. The other came out of books and put a sword made of two wooden slats in his hand, and sent him forth into the benighted world to rescue clear-faced beauty beaten down among rocks.

A great urge to swing out for the good fired his whole inner world, which grew all tender emotion behind the misty form of that dream-lady. He was going to free her from—from some grave peril, or something. It all glowed in the inner sun. He had an image and a mission again!

His world was complete. The outer world was right again.

Galloping forth with the great sword, he would rein sharply and attack from all directions, seeing a sudden distress. "Ha! miscreant—wouldst waylay the fair one?" Whack! "Durst cross with the White Knight? Then, avaunt! take that!—and that!—and *that!*" till the sword of slats broke apart on the ashcan. Then he would go to buy the potatoes.

Goodness became anything desperately oppressed . . . and

he protested when some small boy or girl was being knocked about. Also if a housewife needed help, he ran her errands for her. Anything with woman's complacent face could command him instantly . . . anyone else also if he could get himself to see the need. "Here—a penny for candy; bring me two cigars, no?" "Look—! my clothesline came off." "Mind Conchettina a little while, like a good boy!" But it does not seem to have lasted long, this sort of knight-*errandry*. He liked it better and better with the errand part off. Besides, a burly boy offered him an apron. There was an endless fist-fight in a lot, till both had tired bruised heads.

He took it all with that absurd glow so utterly from within. Hurrah for the true things! Prow to the wave! . . . and he also must create his own material.

"Bang, bang, bang, bang, bang! And forty enemies fell down dead, dying in rolling blood." And the first great manuscript began under his glowing hand, and ended with a sharp twisting of his ear. "Must my stove die waiting for coal?" Then urging the rebellious snarl and quickly repentant tears away, the mother of the wonder-glow awkwardly patted the injured ear—they had always been so united, and were now drifting unreachably apart. Joseph loved this peasant mother because, sobbing in some closet darkness where she had imprisoned him, and nobody loved him any more, nor needed him, he had found in the loneliness of it that he could want her familiar nearness all the more, murmuring his sobs to sleep in this blessedness.

He still had that memory, and it was all that remained of the original protectiveness, the Madonna.

The face of both blended into the image of the true and beautiful which he would defend with his sword . . . and he went to High School consciously a crusader, waiting for some crusade to begin . . . a swordsman waiting.

He thought he was Galahad.

CHAPTER III

A MAN'S BLISTERED HANDS

LOOKING back now, Joseph sees an adolescent who thought he was a stranger in his own kitchen. He was neither American nor Italian; yet he was, simply, both. The explanation goes something like this: when Joseph was at school, he was a boy of the United States going to school; that is, an American boy. And at home he was the son of people of Italy, subject of the Italian law of father-authority.

The melting-pot process seared the father, not the children schooled by the new nation. Yet in the son's first intensity it was very natural for him to write a novel whose theme was, insolently almost, "that the first generation born of foreign people in a new land is a lost generation." There, with that theme, is Joseph, the young reporter. It suggests intense youth, capable of seeing only a half of life.

Praising the book for its true scene and sincerity of feeling, his friend the editor returned it with his indictment: "Not important; pompous," or self-centered; no contribution to the American scene. But his father, writing with gentle understanding of himself and his sons, could have given us the American story.

Another editor, whitening at the temples, felt out the father in the book and sent for the son, saying simply, "I could feel the old gentleman; I love him!" And the son, ashamed, saw that the father was the story, and recast the book, chapter by chapter with the fine old publisher standing by to act as check and gather up the revised whole. But at the end they both saw that the father had been somehow written out of the book.

When the son had let the tensity of youth burn its self-awareness across paper, the father had come up like a portrait in the tumbled writing. But when the son tried again to do the father's portrait as the central point round which to show the family, he did not know how to do it.

And in the ruefulness of that he knew that *he* must have loved the old gentleman, too. But living with him he did not know this. When it came to affection, this family felt awkward. In fact, the children felt strange and if a parent showed them affection they would almost push him away. And among themselves there was not a trace of it. Yet to this day the ache of the least of them is felt by all the others, scattered far away. When they come together again, it is, "How do you feel, all right? are you sure? do you need anything? How is everything, all right?" And the answer, "Aw—" as uneasy as of old; "all right. How's yourself?" And for months on end, no thought of writing. . . .

It is essentially still the same group of an immigrant father —each evolving, trying this and that, getting into those ghastly little muddles and out, getting flung down hard in the unknowable dark, and getting slowly up, to go on once more. . . . Children of a foreigner among us, who found it all a series of kicks in the face and laughs behind his honest back, who did his duty as he saw it, with naturalization papers in his pocket, and his heart often stunned.

"These are the children I created," Joseph's father bitterly summed up. And Joseph saw what the others saw too late: a father, the builder.

The dignity—old-country, but of no country—that is this man, would be hard to define. That is because, we suppose, it is not a quality but a part of the man. He sees you, for instance, to the door, and not till you are safe on the journey and out of sight does he shut it. When he speaks in English with American callers, with his honest slow inability of nearly half a century's effort at English, he pronounces with trouble and uses the longest words—in the most unexpected places.

And yet he could leave all the knowable behind, to come at the age of fifteen to a land of strangers, alone. He said he wandered up and down the Brooklyn streets the day of landing here, with his oilcloth bag in a landlady's room and a piece of bread wrapped up in his pocket, while he set out in foreign silence to look for work, without knowing how to make a start.

"There was a project of track-laying down this street," he said, "and a man laid down his shovel to fell another with his fist, whereupon others dropped tools in commotion, till they fell, with blood of the fists on their faces. Then the boss sent the first man home packing; and seeing me standing there he picked up a shovel and waved it at me, smiling as if explaining what I saw—that he lacked a laborer. And laying my coat folded over the dirt bank, I took and used the shovel among these strange, crisp-spoken men who fell one another down with fists instead of rocks. And they called me Son-neé and Wal-yó, and had calm grins, and made place for me, explaining by motions when the boss wanted me to do a thing. And, working, I revised my world to fit this new one." And he stayed on this project to this day . . . foreman of the street-car rail maintenance project.

Now, much can happen in half a century. But a fifteen-year-old immigrant picking up his first day's shovel could face all the welter of the melting-pot . . . and come through with the same shovel still in hand after forty-nine years, with white hair above a frown, father of his American family still, teaching them the one law he knows: Obey the constituted Caesar.

America does not, cannot understand him. Yet she can and has builded on him, and there is no better understanding than that. And he says with her what is written on coins, sweated dark in his pocket: "In God We Trust."

America, he has saluted you. He gave you the only thing he had, his own, his blistered hands. And these his children.

It was again for Joseph a period of image-making, and the sputtering gurgle of the melting-pot within them, its smudgy steam lending them strange shapes . . . essentially American. They sprang up from a slow borning, in the no-man's-land between opposed worlds, Rome and America.

Let "Nesso," twenty-year-old rebel writer of Joseph's novel recreate for us the border-world and the clashing in an immigrant's kitchen; "Nesso" is Joseph, "Philip" is the first-born Nickey.

"One day I found the counterpart of my father. He was General Washington. He, too, was despoiled of a kingdom, and was forced into hiding with a ragged retinue who swore undying allegiance and hid with him in a snowbound swamp, from whence to pounce between times upon sleek soldiers who sought the General's head. . . .

"I still had my knights, and the castle, and a father who could have been a baronet if he hadn't been born too late. But he had no musket to be fired off on the Fourth of July, and I would have traded the knights and castle for a Redcoat. My old heroes lost their glamour, and became displaced altogether by General Washington, who was the grandest rebel of them all."

And now, the outcome:

"He (the father) had been promoted to new difficulties by the railroad company. And now there was required a daily report of the work he did, and it had to be done in English, on a mass of papers. As this required some knowledge of the American language, he set about on a belated attempt to acquaint himself with the words, but his luck was poor. . . . To make it worse, he eventually gave up the project as a hopeless task, and cursed the American tongue for a devil's invention.

"The result was disastrous to Philip and me. When supper was done one night, he spread out a mass of papers on the table and summoned my brother to construct the report for him.

"Hardly had the two been seated when the kitchen awoke to the sound of a loud cuff, followed by an outcry from Philip and a cry of anger from my father.

" 'Noh, stoopit-a,' came his hard voice, sounding strange with the unaccustomed words. 'No can-da you figuration fo' leel-a ra-ports?'

"There came a sudden scuffle, and Philip retreated to the boys' joint bedroom in tears.

"I gazed at him in the pity that each felt for the other when one of our father's storms descended. Even while I gazed, and tears still welled in his eyes, he fell to chuckling. He stuffed his mouth with the pillow at once, and looked fearfully within. Asked concerning the cause of the punishment, and the unseemly laughter, he replied, 'He told me to write down what he said, but I didn't know what streets he was trying to pronounce. I didn't mean to laugh, but it slipped, and he hit me.' He broke out chuckling again, I joining him loudly. The pillows did not drown the sound entirely. To our great relief, father did not come in.

"Next night, supper cleared, Philip, with a fearsome glance at father, hurried to the stove and began to shake the grate. Father was removing the rubber band from a bundle of ruled papers.

" 'Filippo,' came his gruff command.

" 'I have to fix the fire,' wailed my brother, sending the grate into a great clatter.

" 'Nesso!'

"I went at once.

" 'Fetch the pen and ink—and see that you don't expire on the way!'

"By the kindness of the fates, the articles were found almost at once. I returned to seat myself at his elbow, all aquiver. He pushed several ruled blanks in front of me.

" 'Take the pen and write what I say,' he bade, civilly enough. 'We will make a reporting of the day's accomplishments. There is a division set aside for each appointed subject. We will begin. Noh, first: the date. Put it in: Seven, November, a thousand, nine hundred and thirteen. The—on the top line, pretty of face! There—but certainly!—where else would it be put: on the forehead?'

"I did as I was bidden.

" 'Next, the streets traversed;—and see that you do not do as your brother! There will be a head flying with a sweep! . . . Noh, from—you will write now: beginning on Toomba—Toomba—Temba—but devil take the name!' he protested, after contracting his severe face on it enough. 'Noh, from Timba—Toomba-keets Yeven—.' He scowled at my pen. 'And when?'

"After some hurried debate I wrote Tompkins Avenue.

" '*Si*,' he agreed, immediately having inspected it. 'Toombakeenas. Noh, we tore up old rail beginning from the traverse of, noh: Bairga Streets,—but put it down.'

"I decided on Bergen Street.

" 'And this is it,' he decided, nodding. 'Noh, from there to Err—Urrkumonna Streets. Put it down.'

"I struggled with the sound. It refused to take shape in my mind. The frown drove me to desperation.

" 'Does it begin with a U, or an E?' I floundered, grasping at straws.

" 'It is to begin again?' he threatened. 'We will have it begin with a fan on the ear! Noh, Err-kumonna; Oor-kamenna—. But write, lump of American nothing!'

"With difficulty keeping back a beginning blubber that would rise, I wrote: Irkman Street. But he at once bent such a challenging frown on it that my blubberings rose.

" 'Noh, what is this composition here?' he would know sharply. 'Did I say: Eerkamenna? I said: *Oork*—'

" 'I don't know what to write,' I wept in rebellion, 'you don't say it right.'

" 'Ghost of your mother!' he burst, with a head-jarring

sweep of his open hand. And was up striding in a wrath that made us all huddle. 'For this I sweat my blood, to keep you in the schools of this accursed land! Better that I send these to pick up coals in the lots, like your betters of the colony! Who washes the head of a donkey loses the time and the soap;—be off to bed, *miserabile!*'

"Philip and I, making common cause to ward off further calamity, knocked the copper bottom out of mother's wash boiler. This metal we took to the ragman. With the proceeds of this business we bought a city guide, that listed not only the streets of Brooklyn, but the surface railway lines as well. By hard study that day we committed every carline-street to memory. The first thing I looked up was the street that had terrorized last evening. It was, merely, Herkimer Street. Father's pronunciation lost its terror.

"The end of father's official struggle with the English language came sharply on a blasting blowsy day in winter. It was so cold he dismissed his crew and came home, where we huddled for such warmth as the kitchen stove afforded.

"Father, home for any length of time, would grow either a despair on nerves prepared for a storm, or he would suddenly sweetly be himself, come free from the torments of hard life that pressed him so. And when he was thus released he was—he was sweet, what other word will do? Almost a boy. He developed sudden strange hungers, and would go get and cook the most sudden things—wildly bitter small onions, chestnuts, eels, smoked bloaters—anything. And droll, lightsome, sunny, laughing stories such as yet dimly echoed from the time when Madonna had been. Then how we did blink . . . and run flocking about him.

"This forenoon, we hovered about expecting a grim homecoming frown, barometer of whippings, as his heavy measured tread came up the halls. But he came in with such a contented ease behind the bitten vivid cheeks and wind-cut eyes, that it was as if the sun had burst on fog.

" 'Toh!—how rosy she glows, Catarina,' he grinned, stopping in the door in his burly coat and fur hat. Catarina was the stove. 'Help me out of the coats—the finger of the ice wind is thrust up my back amid them!' And how we gleefully ran tugging! It would be a rare day.

"Scarcely had he thawed his feet against Catarina, when he cheerily called Philip and me.

" 'Noh, papa,' he beamed, 'bundle yourselves in your warmest garments, and go to the store to fetch me some (and he named it in English) *mell ice.*'

"He gave us a fifty-cent piece, and we went. One never asked our father to pronounce an English word twice. But down in the blast of the winds Philip looked dubiously at me. 'What the dickens is mell ice?'

" 'Something to eat,' I promptly said. 'He feels good.'

"We went to the American stores to get some. From store to store in the northwest blow that tried to sweep us off. We went as far as Elton Street down Atlantic Avenue from Eastern Parkway, and back up Fulton, and came back empty-handed, miserable, and stung cold. Nobody, it seemed with knowing blinks or blank stares, had ever heard of mell ice; one who kept nodding and nodding thoughtfully to himself over it did say, 'Oh yes, ah yes; did you say *mell* ice? We just sold the last.'

" 'He don't know what it is,' decided my brother outside.

We began to whimper in the cold. We'd get a beating, upstairs.

"We headed into the home block. That would put us into the sweeping wind. We took a step into it and it blew us into a store doorway, sobbing with cold and dread. The doors were pulled open and a small wrinkled berry-faced man said, 'Ach! gome in yet.'

"The kindness and the warm air made us cry. We told him of the useless quest.

" 'Hm,' he said, with a thoughtful frown. 'Mell ize, hey? Himmel!' It was a drug store and he looked about it wondering, then he went to the counter and around it, saying, 'I dink what he wants I know alretty—he shust right didn't said it.' He sent us home to get a bottle for it; he kindly explained that would save us five cents. 'The boddle from before.'

"Delivered, we flew down the block, wind or no.

" 'To Naples,' father frowned at once, 'I thought you had gone for the purchase. Let me have it.'

"We told him of the bottle. And by the cloud on his face we instantly—

" 'What signifies this bottle!'

" 'It comes in bottles now,' I hastened to explain.

"Mother hurriedly instituted a search . . . which yielded from under somewhere a dusty large sodawater bottle. At this the druggist scowled.

" 'Why didn't you bring a pail?' he grumbled, and went behind his partition without the bottle. He emerged with a small wrapped bottle and did it up with druggist paper and string.

"Father took the bottle with a searching frown from the

first-born. My heart sank. He fairly tore the paper off.

" 'Magnesia!' he burst at once.

"He hurled the bottle into the sink, where it exploded. Then in a frightful stillness he bundled himself warmly and left the house, to return very quickly. He strode through the door . . . and put down on the table a bulky object, wrapped up, like a can. He summoned Philip and me, grimly.

" 'Noh, what is that which in five minutes I can bring?" he demanded, with a force that made flesh quiver.

"Trembling, unwilling fingers drew the paper off. It was a squat round can with a blue label.

" 'Molasses—' said Philip despite himself, it was so sudden.

"Then father's crispness fell, like whip lashes.

" 'Noh, attend, *ignoranti:* tomorrow you will take a letter to Signor Tosti, he who takes private scholars. It took you two hours to bring magnesia; I found molasses in five minutes. And I never went to the schools of this country. The American schools have taught you nothing. I'll make you a school! Italian you were born, and Italian you will remain;—bring me the paper and ink!'

"I knew of Signor Tosti. He was a parched old man in skull cap and slippers, who locked one up for hours on end in a hot room that smelled of mattresses, and gave hard problems, and impressed them with a broad belt which he wore with the buckle behind, using such vigor in producing scholars that once one escaped he never passed the old man's street again. Into the bargain, he taught nothing but Italian. In such a place, my idols would find small welcome.

" 'I'm American, this is where I was born,' I cried, from what revolt nobody knows, except that I could feel it surging even in a burst of tears, 'I won't learn Italian instead of English—I won't—!'

"And realizing the rashness I stood still . . . as in a mist I beheld my father's rugged face of unbelief go dark; ever an authority to be obeyed, now he was defied. And with blood receding I shut my eyes as he thrust our protesting mother aside and bore down lashing with wrath . . . and the braided clothesline fell, rose and fell in a haze.

"I came to with ears whistling. From somewhere came a wail which separated into the wailing of sisters and brother. Then remembering I scrambled up and ran to mother, who pressed me to her side with a white face of silence standing like a wall before father.

"But it seemed not to be needed. He stood as if it was he who had been lashed, with lips that opened to speak.

"Then without a word he opened the window to the rush of cold and flung the braided clothesline whip into it.

" 'To teach them I must drive them from me,' he said with tears in his eyes. And walking away he left us full of a sudden silence."

Joseph substantially depicted the spirit of the clash. It cast a shadow over the house. It made him feel as a son should not feel. He seemed to be able to find no way to go to his mother and father, as other sons did, and have a talk. They did not speak the same language . . . in more than one sense. Both he and Nickey had run into hard whippings. Some of them were because youth would go this way and that way, but they did not know that till later. They resented the rule of the whip.

But it was, must have been, for the father, anguish itself.

He wanted to teach them respect. And he saw that he was whipping up rebellion instead.

And the lesson went home. They learned about duty and could thank him quietly . . . twenty years later, when the father's teachings cropped out in ghastly failures, like bedrock.

But first they were to fill him with bitterness that must have made him want to cry out sometimes from its unbearable cup.

For one son of this just man went seedy on a trail of horse bets and sour wine; the other sold him.

Chapter IV

THE BLIND AND THE LAME

The breach widened with adolescence.

Quoting Joseph's novel again:

"Of this I am sure: that father realized there was a breach between us no quicker than I did. It parted so gradually that, being both on separate brinks of it, we were not aware that there was a gap till it could not be crossed.

"He finally permitted me to go through the whole course of education in the schools of his adopted country. But he equipped from his sweat a stranger to his Italy, who brought America clashing into his kitchen. Sending forth a son with bread, the son came back with a stone.

"And neither of them had wanted that. That is the hell of it."

Aye, says Joseph;—hell for the father.

Things grew slowly, smouldering for a flash. But providentially the President called for crusaders to make the world safe. And leaving college plans behind, Joseph at the age seventeen listened, and must have found the old wooden sword still there. For he jumped over the kitchen breach, enlisting in a regiment.

The oldest Pigtail, calmest of the house, and quite American, guessed the news from his face and advised him not to come home at the moment. "Somehow he knows you went to sign up. That's a lot of American in one lump. It won't digest."

Joseph's surge of crusade-glow left him suddenly. But a deep-seated reaction took place. His father, sensing Joseph's plan to offer himself as a soldier, had told him plainly that this was a declaration of independence. Somehow it was not so much that it involved open profession of being American, as that it would bring the question of loyalty to a father's ideal to the test. That ideal they all understood very well. It was obedience to constituted authority. It was being the son of a son of Italy. It was letting evolution work itself out along Italian lines, that taught duty at all cost. The son had snarled more than once, "I can't help what I am; what do I know about Italy? It's a whole world away. I'm born of this country. I'm American. And they stuck me in an Italian house and talk about duty till I'm sick of it. Why can't we let it go at that and let us try to go together?" Always in English, that speech, always a swordthrust through the father.

Joseph understood well enough that enlistment would be interpreted as an overthrow of his father's authority. He had disobeyed, gone the other way. It was not the joining of a war regiment, primarily; Mr. Tired's honest heart was with the cause. Both for Italy and America he was for the cause. But he was being openly dishonored; a son refused to obey.

Joseph, pondering these things in the stunned sensibility of youth, slept that night in a woodland park under a culvert running swiftly with a heavy rain. There was a shoulder of dry earth against a curving wall, on which he spread some newspapers which he had taken out of a trash bin. Near him was a hobo, driven off his usual park bench by the rain. The hobo slept not at all that night. Whenever Joseph woke up he found the unclean man sitting up to smoke cigarette-ends out of a baking-powder can.

Toward dawn the burly sentinel of the youth's effort to sleep spoke up to ask out of his cigarette glow, "Got folks, Bub?"

"Yes," was torpor's reply.

"Trouble?" After a pause the man went on, "It ain't cop trouble, I can see that. You ain't the park kind. And I ain't butting in. I'm old enough. You didn't sleep much; so I know you didn't settle the trouble yet."

"I guess I never will." From afar, from aloneness.

"That's what I figured. I saw your clothes, and you sitting on that bench, letting people pass, and all that. Then all of a sudden I thought, 'He ain't in the blues, it's trouble, he's going to sleep here tonight.' It didn't jibe. I couldn't make it fit with girl trouble. It wouldn't fit. They don't sleep in parks, when the girl goes out on them. You never slept outside before."

"I never was out of my home bed before," stated Joseph.

"That's what I thought quick."

Joseph thought the man through. He was blotted out somewhere behind the spark of a cigarette-end. Joseph wanted suddenly not to be left alone in a cessation of talk.

But silence continued. . . . Joseph rolled over amid the papers and tried to sleep. It was no good. He sat up and lit a cigarette. The bum was putting a spark-end out in the dirt.

The man said, "Father trouble?"

"Yes."

"Uh, huh." The man paused. He said suddenly, in earnest, "Did *he* say it never can be settled?"

Joseph, taken abruptly, replied after a moment, "You wouldn't understand."

"Correct. No son ever does." The man went on after a long silence, "You didn't sleep so good, because I'm a tramp."

But Joseph saw a sentry. "You saw me through,—sitting up to—" Then quietly, "Thanks. You didn't have to."

"I was thinking, meself. I'm a son, too. Maybe you don't think so, seeing a dirty old drifter sleeping around halls and places. But I was your age, once, and it couldn't patch up for a cent—I thought. And I guess he didn't sleep any better than I did, waiting for me to come home, where I left him in a rush. . . . He's prob'ly a long time dead now, Dad, waiting there for me. It couldn't be patched up. Why, hell— He wiped it all off the second I busted off with him. They forgive the shot in the face, before they fall."

There was silence.

Joseph said abruptly, "I just joined the army—he's old-school Italian. It's been a fight over being American— And this is throwing his authority over at last, I guess."

"Going to France, you think?" ignoring the question. The matter-of-factness blessed Joseph, made him calm.

"Yes."

"Suppose you get killed? . . ." He added gently, "The last you saw him was, standin' there where you left him. Do you think you can face that, across the trenches? . . . I'm wishing, kid," he wearily said, "I'd gone back, and faced the punch in the face. What the hell? What's a father for? I let him stand there, waiting."

Silence returned. Joseph resisted a jammed throat that wanted to shout out. . . .

Sun flooded the muddy archway when he sat up startled among papers. He was alone under a culvert in a park.

He felt sticky, dirty and strained when he stood up brushing his blue-serge wrinkles, and searching for his hat. He felt strange in a world of loneliness. Birds chirped. One flew through the culvert out of the dawn sun, rustling.

Joseph turned adrift and washed his face at the drinking fountain. He was wetting his handkerchief again to cool his temples when the burly soiled man came, pausing with earnestness, as if he would speak. Instead he nodded and drank.

Again as he turned to go away, he seemed to hesitate. Then as he started away under his torn hat, Joseph burst out eagerly: "I'm going back—."

Father was at his coffee when Joseph opened the door and stood within, the door shut behind. The heavy-shouldered man slowly put down his coffee. He looked tired and troubled, with relief in the first glance. But in the silence grimness returned.

"Noh," he commanded, "where were you?"

"In the park."

"And a bed you had not? A house you have not?"

"I didn't think I had a right to come to it."

The father looked his trouble at him. He arose heavily, picking up his hat. "Noh, mark that a heart of guilt is its conviction of guilt. . . . And now what?"

"I don't know." Joseph's lips trembled. "What can I say? You said to enlist was against you, and I enlisted."

The father's troubled face grew more troubled. He looked at his son.

"All these burdens I must bear," he said; "but *malditto* the father who would shoulder them. . . . Noh," he asked, "to France do you go, do you know?"

"After they call—I'm on the regiment's reserve list."

"This is the bed prepared by yourself," he said wearily. He put on his slouch hat of many years' dignity. "Try not to upset your mother—if they call, they call; what they command you to do, thus do; you have sold yourself for a soldier, you understand. . . . Noh, have your eggs and coffee. And go to bed."

These grim fathers—where are they?

Joseph came back from France with a spring in his step, and the great glow that is youth in the sun. As the parade of the overseas regiments on Decoration Day broke up, he waved at a young woman who had flung him a rose. With the bugler who had headed a platoon of the parade beside him, Joseph went with the young woman and her woman companion to their apartment. But he grew uncomfortable in the house of these two wives of other men . . . and found himself muttering, adrift out in the sun of the park again. The same thing had happened again and again in France, and before that in Brooklyn, when youth had gone seeking a woman in some open house. Always in sudden unease he had gone drifting away, alone. He just couldn't— Just couldn't.

It may have been childhood's image of cleanness on high, or boyhood's womanhood or the Galahad's beautiful and true that needed a swordsman for defender. In youth's street they had jeered, in France they shrugged. At the joint apartment they had merely given a look, with surprise behind it.

It had happened again in the same woodland park of the culvert, where with that sun still in his eyes he sat adrift, pulling up clovers, beside an overseas entertainer who finally pouted queerly, "You're on the right track, after all . . . but you won't know that yet. Wish you luck to the end." And wandered rhythmically away among the trees, untaken, her crooked bit of smile troubling him. And it was suddenly a conglomerate image smiling . . . telling him to go on.

Joseph, under the trees, got up and drifted away. "I'm waiting for her," he thought suddenly.

Going home with an involuntary army quick-step, he could picture her: lithe, clear-faced, laughing-eyed. And suddenly chucking the chin of a baby on her lap.

It probably was nothing more . . . or less . . . than any man's vague picture of waiting for the one woman.

It had happened the last time in a rubber town across the Alleghanies.

Wanderlust called Joseph out after adventure. Longing seems to have died, however, when the companion of the adventure, who had been his fellow-sergeant, turned out to be a slave to wages. They did not go to the Oklahoma oil fields because the money they were earning in the rubber shop steadied down toward one hundred dollars a week, each. "Boob" C. had at first invited him along, when it was a woman he wanted, and suddenly there was a snarling quarrel that left them silenced across the bed they sat on. And in the pain of words that cannot be recalled, Joseph said slowly, "You have me wrong—as wrong as they had me in France. It wasn't a pledge I took, and it wasn't greenness, it wasn't apron strings; I thought I didn't know what it was but I know now. I'm waiting for the girl I'll meet somewhere, some day, out from inside me . . . where I suppose I've been building her up. I don't blame you for sticking it into me. It sounds cracked."

And he picked up his hat to drift out. Boob's hand came down on his shoulder. He offered his hand, simply. He said in the surprise of it, "I'd give all I'd get, for an ideal like that to get me through." He added strangely, "I understand what you meant in Angoulême, when you said you'd joined a crusade, and we guffawed."

Some things seem to crop out like that, out of the flimsiest mists.

She did step out, from wherever such beings evolve, to walk forth across the sun to him, smiling.

It was on the sidewalk before Luna Park, in the tinsel and wonder-glow of a Coney Island night. This was organization week and the American Legion were selling tickets for Luna Park, making fifty cents on each strip.

She had a girl-smile with the hint of a proud pout, a tilted little black turban over wide eyes, brown in sun-sparkle, and a vivid small mouth, that parted smiling as if to say, "I came as soon as I could."

Joseph knew that instantly, though what she did say was, archly enough, "You'll have to step on the gas, then, I'm miles ahead of you." Joseph was also selling tickets.

And with that twisty bit of smile she stopped seven sailors and sold them a ticket-strip each for Luna, priced at double the usual price.

Joseph, wandering into a post meeting in quest of a cause, had found one in the blunt Commander's fling at sheepish men: "You cheap bunch of ——s! Up goes a drive for dough, to get us started, and a bunch of women stuck out there facin' that Coney Island mob, alone. And the turn-out of this post to help them push them double-price tickets is one half a man —a guy with a leg off. Why, you —— ——! It's a waste o' me breath—; but I'm wondering if there's just one guy in this outfit that can feel cheap enough to crawl down there tonight and the rest of the week and help get the money that women strangers are getting for us: I'm talking to that man now;— the rest of you can go to hell. And that's plump and plain. Comrade adjutant, read the minutes."

About forty men quit that meeting and humbly asked tickets to sell, of the stout and cheery young-mother lady who was in charge of the girls. And at the end of the drive-week Joseph had outsold all the rest . . . topping the real ticket-seller who had been leading, by more than fifty dollars net.

And that was the girl who had stepped diagonally across in front of him out of the wreathing mists within him.

She came next day, a Sunday, to shake the coin-can for the Salvation Army with him, he in her jaunty bit of black turban, she in his fore-and-aft overseas hat. And they breasted the festa mobs in the glass-light glow, and went staggering side by side in the surges, and called for coins till they were hoarse at two A.M. . . . whereupon the One who works these wonders in the sudden places of life must have called it a day, and gone gently away.

For they suddenly could not end the side-by-side chore in the jam of life . . . and over a lingering handclasp their eyes begged it not to end, and in a quick calm smile it did not. "We'll come another night, for ourselves." And she said quickly, "Why not now? We have a whole hour or two yet, before they lock up the Coney sidewalk for the morning." And hand in hand Twenty and Eighteen took in as many of the rides as could be crammed into two so-short hours, laughing like any children.

And father, seeing the uprush from the supper table lest the 6:56 express to the other county be missed, would growl, "But what is so urgent—?"

"It's a girl," Joseph would say. And the father would growl again, "But two mouthfuls is supper; a girl more important?"

When it happened steadily enough the father detained his son. "It is no girl, is it the woman of serious intention?"

And Joseph told him, knowing it was hard to hear, for the girl was of the American strangers. "And among the damsels of your people, there is not one to make you a home?"

Then there would be unease and worried faces, for the answer was always the same, "It came that way—it wouldn't make any difference if she were blue or yellow. Father, I *love* the woman."

"Why don't you give her the air?" growled Nickey. "You see the trouble it's causing. You don't know who she is, what kind of wise one putting it all over you—"

"I don't have to know,—and if you weren't my brother I'd make you swallow that back damn' quick—"

"You know I didn't mean it that way," quietly. He added gently, "Think it over."

But Joseph continued to bolt for the 6:56. There was a 7:15

and a 7:49 also stopping at her suburban station. But she would be absolutely waiting for him in her mother's house on the 6:56 . . . or drifting and humming about the station green, with quick face turning around to meet the flash of his across the green. And drifting they found themselves walking hand in hand, and people turned to gaze back smiling. They walked here and there, or saw open-air picture shows, a vaudeville, a fair, or birds chirping on tree boughs. She watched him carving a heart on a park bench, in wonder, with their initials under. They sought that bench with their first-born, years later, and laughed at the carved heart.

Between these two scenes there was a violent upheaval.

It came on the wedding night. Her mother and sisters were there waiting with his army friend and the Episcopalian chaplain of some war regiment, in his chapel. At home his father had pleaded with him. Both were soon in tears. His father's words echoed in his mind: "You must choose between a father and a stranger of strangers." But Joseph wanted both.

In a haze he had kissed his mother and turned sharply around to go. "I don't want these things to happen—I'm still trying to be your son—" And left them huddled there, and went to slip the ring on her finger with a smile over the ache, the lone representative of his house.

An odd thing happened. The ring refused to go on. The finger was smooth and even and wonderful to hold. The ring was the right size. But it would not pass the slight rise of knuckle. He urgently tugged. The rector in his robes had to stop his reading. Suddenly it went on and looked beautiful—plain thin gold on cream. His eyes misted. It had cost enough but it was worth it.

The rector said abruptly, "It went on hard. God grant it may come off as hard."

Then simply he finished the sitting-room service.

A year later Joseph was jobless and broke, and homesick. Whether it was the homesickness that turned him back he does not know. But suddenly he was standing in his father's kitchen, with the woman of the Americans beside him, the first-born in her arms. And the mother nearly dropped the soup dish she was carrying.

At her cry of unbelief and gladness, the father came in from waiting for the soup, with the sisters and brothers behind him. He stood stock still, his rugged face beset with trouble at this home-coming.

"Noh," he bade in silence, "where-sa you be keep youself?"

"Around."

The father's perpetual frown looked at the two standing with the bundled baby. He seemed more rugged, more weary.

"Noh, seat for eatcha soup-a, wit you brudd' hand sist'." To the mother he said quietly, "See hif you can-da help you daughta which he bringin' to you." And in Italian he commanded her, "Go, receive your daughter."

And tears whipped the eyes of the American whose gaze turned to Joseph at this.

That was all, that is all there was to it. Only fools will explain the melting-pot.

Chapter V

FAMILY MAN

A chart of Joseph, as a breadwinner, would show such a sharp-pointed jag of ups and downs, that only a madman could find the mean average line of it all. Years later a self-mocking Joseph was to try making a graph of the first years, but it looked so much like a corkscrew that he wandered off and sat down somewhere to smoke the torpor away.

But all his world agree that those were the sweet years, the married years of a couple of children. They were the wonder years, the dismayed and always astonished and somehow brave years of a union that suddenly was no more.

Perhaps it was just youth, wondering what it's all about —and full of the tremendous responsibility of caring for the real-live woman and baby that had been trusted to him. It seemed a beautiful eternity, but that's exactly what makes the backward-glancer sad. It was such a short while. . . .

The honeymoon peculiarly fitted this thing of wonder that had begun under the Luna glow. Her mother and sisters saw the two to the subway kiosk, he in his blue suit that he had had made particularly for this event, and a—a derby; she in a tan suit that was just right for her proudly trustful slim person; and the party shouted after them and drowned the upcoming rush of people, throwing bags of sudden rice and a shoe. With rice in his derby brim he escorted his charge through the chasm of the subway, but not to the far-away honeymoon land which they let everyone think was the goal; oh, no. They went to a hotel near Central Park, and spent the winter honeymoon on benches, feeding peanuts to the squirrels, four days, cuddling up warmly together and staring in wonder at people with sudden friendly grins, at policemen who were sentries of their oneness, and at a man in hobo grime who spent an hour with them, wished them happiness, shook hands with each, and stood there in the gravel path till they waved back from the bend. That was the wonder of this honeymoon in winter under bare boughs: everybody understood it perfectly, and had a smile for them . . . and probably knew it would be one of those young and wonderful things that somehow get through crashes that smash wiser weddings. Among the abrupt well-wishers was the keeper of the monkey-house.

Life assailed this wonder-world at once. All he had for bulwark was a great urge and $2.70. The board was $20 a week against a $25 salary as keeper of the accounts of the gasoline and oil consumed by the fleet of trucks of a chain grocery firm. He was not fitted for clerical detail. The job began to chafe; try as he might there would always be some detail forgotten. When the office frowns grew too glowering he put an advertisement in the newspapers, from which came a job of starting an advertising department for a paper and blotter distributor. They wanted a line of booklets and blotters that were "different." He created a line that was exactly that. Nobody knew just what the lay-out was, it was so different. Then the partners called him down to wipe up a great black stain on the floor where a bottle of ink had burst; the porter was home ill for the day, they said. The demobilized Top Sergeant and creator of art shot his chin out. "You go to hell," he said, and went up in some dignity to put on his scarf, derby and coat. They were still standing there when he came down; the elderly and pleasant-faced partner looked disturbed, the lean bilious one glowered. But Joseph knew they had found his effort at advertising wanting. "If my work was no good, why didn't you come right out and say so? Kneel down and wipe up your floor yourself." And he strode out. He was shaky with rebellion—and felt the singing void that grows on one found wanting.

She said indignantly, "What 'o they think—? I'm glad you had spunk enough. . . . Never mind, dear," her arm round him urged, "you'll be somebody big some day—for me and Tommy." Tommy was the baby on the way. That was the name decided on in the first three months.

Somebody invented a windshield wiper working out of the air of the manifold or exhaust or something. They needed a hand to keep account of the cash and of the outgo. They were two brothers, plain and honest workingmen, who rented a window and frosted it and mounted their wiper to slosh back and forth slowly across the clean arc of visibility. They looked at Joseph in thought and consulted, and said, "$22 a week." And he kept accounts in what he called bookkeeping books, which by mutual experiments grew to be a fairly understandable chart of finances. They had wanted a bookkeeper, but they said to Joseph after a month, "You're honest, and trying hard for us. If we grow you'll grow with us; we don't know much about office work, so try to figure out a system for us."

"Do your best for them, they're depending on you," urged his lady, concerned for the brothers who depended on her man.

Then suddenly people with more money forced them to sell out. The wiper is seen on cars all over the world today. It was Joseph's first education in legalized ruthlessness.

Joseph was looking for a situation. Tommy was about five months on the way. They went from housekeeping apartments to mere furnished rooms. They were happy, but for the memory of the tired father standing in tears in the kitchen, where Joseph had left him . . . Joseph kept the mails filled with wonderful short-stories written in a tremendous urge from his image-world. He was to be discovered suddenly, he knew. She thought her man wonderful. She had always a proud hint of it in her face. Her high-heel step was full of proud confidence. He thought his lady wonderful . . . and trembled when he held this wonder in his arms. To be trusted with this trust and Tommy, gee—

Suddenly in the spring there was no odd job even and no room rent. The landlady-of-the-moment gave permission to pack up their suitcase. They stood in the setting sun beside a subway kiosk, that evening, in the immense and heavily peopled barrenness of Park Row. In his pocket was the address of a Greek contractor who might have a job for him—and thirty-five cents. He had broken with his father and could not face him now. They had nowhere to sleep; their goods were what was contained in the suitcase on the sidewalk by the kiosk, amid surging endless people.

Joseph's glow-world fell in ruins.

Turning to the troubled girl beside him he said, bitterly, "A fine breadwinner—; I haven't even got a place for you to sleep." She was startled out of her stillness. He said less resolutely but with absolute directness, "Listen—. I have no more right to you. I have failed you. You must go to your people. Go back. When I can make you as comfortable as you were before you married me, then I'll come back and claim you. Now I've got no more right. You've got to go back."

Her face of startled pain alarmed him. Tears whipped across her eyes.

"I will not—! And leave you when you need help most—? What 'o you think—?" And blurted wabbly phrases amid staring Gotham. "Did I ask anything—? Did I kick? What you have I have—what you bring me is all I want—; did I kick? You're all I want, only you—; go ahead and get rid of me if you don't want me any more—" And sobs tumbled out, all jolted up from pain.

Joseph took her in his arms, overswept by this that asked nothing, only needed to be accepted; she was carrying his baby right now. And stunned he pillowed the sobs against his shoulder. There in the midst of the evening rush-hour. And in a blur he muttered at the stares of troubled New York, "Aw—go 'way, let us alone—"

They spent ten of the thirty-five cents and rode to the beach at Coney Island. There on the sands he sat, the bed for her cuddled body and for Tommy. And a jibbering restless Frenchman in a straw hat paced the surf all night with a stick. He woke them in red warm dawn-glow, got them laughing with a queer lot of soldier-jokes and sayings, patted them many times rapidly on the shoulder and hurried away.

They washed at the drinking fountain and spent ten more of the twenty-five cents for a cup of coffee and a bun. Then gently he left her to wait by the beach, to go try the Greek contractor in the Bronx. By the grace of the magi of Gotham, five cents would take a Joseph all the way from Coney to the Bronx, some fourteen miles. But at the rich man's apartment the wife and servants quietly said he was at the hospital. Then seeing how troubled he stood there, they called up over the telephone and decided he could go see him.

The Greek received him in his convalescent's suite. "For a job you must come to a hospital patient. You are very unexperience' of the world. What kind of work you have thought to do?" But Joseph did not know; anything; a job—he must have a job.

There was a pause. The Greek was troubled. . . . "My poor youth, what I can give you? Could I say to a bookkeeper: 'Here, I have a pick and shovel'? Yet I can offer to such as you, nothing else."

Joseph in a blur saw his lady-and-Tommy waiting there for a man who had only himself to give. "I'll take the shovel," he said.

But the man was suddenly disturbed. He sat up slowly, a shapeless bulk of bedrobes. "You would take the shovel—you?"

"I've got to— And be glad."

The man looked steadily back. Then he turned and picked up the telephone. . . . And a man came with money, and he counted out fifty dollars into Joseph's stunned hand. "Take it for advance wages. I believe in you."

It remained as the finest bit of human longing to be the brother's keeper that Joseph had found.

They took the night boat up the Hudson to the headwaters, finishing the journey by train. He took the shovel. After four days the master mechanic in general charge, who had been standing studying his constructing a short ditch alone, called him and sent him moving along with a pipe-laying crew who followed a steam-shovel. After a while he was again promoted, this time to be fireman on a locomotive crane. And the Greek stood nodding a bit of greeting from the ground.

Tommy arrived in a farmer's attic in the mountains. He was called Gilbert for her brother, because neither of the sisters had called their sons after Gil. Only one thing clouded the homely peace up there, and that was Joseph's father, who had been left standing in tears in his kitchen. But Joseph was learning to lie in the bed he had made.

The fire in the crane kept dying under Joseph's clerical hand. One crane turned over as it lifted a weight while Joseph was supposed to stand off and see that the weight did not tilt the crane-truck off the tracks. Another crane scorched its boiler, and always the union complained of him as an outsider. The master mechanic put him at the project switchboard, plugging calls to an army constructing a dam, and to the colony of wives of officials who at noon must be warned to go away while blasted rock fragments rained about.

An incident occurred. Wandering free one noon, Joseph crossed a desert of rock outcroppings. And something in him caught a far shout of anguish . . . and across the wide shallow stream a desperate man flung himself upon the powder-man crouching to pull a switchbox. For Joseph was drifting over a stone-crop packed with half a ton of dynamite. "My God, boy—," panted the man, who had run across the work-bridge and punched him, "I didn't mean it—it was relief. I don't know what got me to look up from my lunch and see you drifting over it, 'way out across there."

But Joseph later could glimpse within these overalls a guardian angel.

One day Joseph forgot to warn just one cottage of the forty-odd cottages, when a blast was going off. And a rock fragment burst through the flimsy roof and frightened an expectant mother, who was wife of the superintendent. Then Joseph was looking for a job again, in a town of strangers, for a wife and for Gil.

Then suddenly the girl-mother could stand no more, overcome as she was by insecurity and homesickness. There was just enough to send the wife and baby home to her mother; while Joseph made his way to Albany to find work enough to send himself home.

The great rail strike of that year was declared outlawed, men filled the Rensselaer yards, a replacement army of the men who had walked out. Joseph got in there, sleeping with four hundred in a converted barracks because flying stones made it unsafe to leave.

In two months of overtime and double-time wages Joseph was able to join his wife and son with considerable funds for a start. The money soon melted away, however. Lacking a trade he went as a yardman on the Long Island Railroad, staying till an idea evolved. The best place for a fairly educated man with resolution seemed to be the field of salesmanship.

Then came three years of the hand-to-mouth existence of the canvasser. And three years of stories that never sold, and of the writing of his novel. He sold coal, flower bulbs, pencils, wire brushes, perfumes, magazine subscriptions—anything.

They moved from rooming-house to small furnished apartment, and then back to a single room, endlessly, suiting convenience to the moment's luck. At last they contracted to buy furniture on the instalment-plan and went into a flat by themselves. When earnings fell too low at last, the wagon came and took the stuff away. He found his wife sitting on the floor with the baby in the bare living-room, and she suddenly burst into tears.

Joseph was profoundly shaken. He was giving this woman who depended on him, nothing but let-downs; she had nothing on which to depend. And she would still bravely smile, longing to believe in him still.

The simple faith of that stunned him. And a Jew who for weeks had tried to sell them a rug or a chair or a string of beads or something, walked in with his seared old face and young ideas, and stared at the two sitting alone against the wall. "My, my, my—dey tooked it out; what 'o you tink o' dot! Not even a chence! . . . So, vot kind furniture you like? Four rooms? . . . Heh, heh, heh—look how dey get excided!" he chuckled. And he urged, "Dun'd vorry. Life ain'd vort' it. Alvays efter de rain it shines, de sun—. How you'll pay on notting? Dun'd I know it you got hard luck a while?—ve all got it again and again—dot's vot ve are for, to give a hend ven somevun is stuck. Dun'd I know your parents? Heh, heh, heh! Only t'irty years I been trying to sell your fodder somet'ing—und now I sell his son. . . . Come right avay down togedder; ve ride to the store und pick out de furniture, your vord is de down payment—heh, heh, heh, heh. . . ."

Good old Gittelson. With his laugh and his many troubles.

Joseph saw that he was failing in his trust. Five years, she had given him of herself, her all . . . and insecurity and blurts of tears had come of it.

"Look—; I've thought it over," he suddenly told her. "I'm getting old. I'm twenty-five. All my father had was his two hands, he didn't have a dime, couldn't even speak the language here. And yet he built a home for his woman, bought two chairs and a table, a bed and a trunk, for cash, and went out to work, no favors asked and none looked for. What he has is his, he built it. He's the one foreman the B.R.T. can trust. Rain or shine or a storm or what, he's out there demanding that the work come out just right; it's got to pass his own idea of honesty or he won't pass it at all. He quit in a huff after a quarter century and they came and sent for him; it's absolutely against all B.R.T. tradition or any business-world tradition. Why? He's exactly what he'll always be, himself—an honest man giving himself with his hands. He built up a thing no man can ever take away from him; respect. The B.R.T. respects him, a greenhorn from Italy."

"So what—? You've thought it over and . . . ?"

"I'm going to start right now, building something you can depend on. No more running around selling something nobody wants, no more hanging up bills till some wages come in. I'm going on the cash-on-the-table plan. I'm sick and tired of this no-trade business, no calling. That's what. I've decided the one thing I can do and be useful in my own way, spreading a word of cheer around while doing it. A solid income that you can count on in advance, and a visible means of support. I've thought it over."

"What is it?"

"Letter carrier. Uncle Sam can be counted on, by a wife."

There was something of a glow in the gray-uniformed mission. The work was something he could grip, feel, handle, turn over. It was tangible. People anxiously waiting morning after morning for the one letter; sudden death messages and the rushes of joy; letters calling troubled people to work and letters dashing their hopes; and home-coming messages, and summons to sick-beds. And bills. Joseph reacted every day to his letters and the people behind them. That is why he loved the work. And when Christmas rush-time came, all the substitutes went down to the contract stable for a horse and wagon to deliver the packages; and reins in hands, behind his steed, he would get into impossible jams and out again with his lopsided green wagon and horse. The more the trolley cars and automobiles raged behind, the more resolved he grew, in his gray uniform, to stick his visor-capped head out of the side and shout, "Ah, go to hell." You can't hurry a horse, and people want Christmas packages delivered.

But Uncle Sam could not be counted on by his wife after all. For though he paid exceedingly promptly, substitute letter-carriers earned only when a regular man failed to appear. Many mornings Joseph would wait hoping someone was temporarily sick, or called somewhere by relatives, or moved to take a day off, but waited in vain. The regulars showed up at their posts so regularly. . . . And Tommy was on the way again, this time with the wistful hope that he would be a girl. She said confidently, "It'll be a girl, for you. I've got a feeling."

He was on edge the day the child was born, out with the letters somewhere. She had suddenly looked ill. "I'll be all right," she had urged. But that was it—she had coaxed him to believe that. Therefore, reasoned the Joseph who suspected all things, it was *not* all right. Suddenly toward the winter's dusk he was convinced it was all wrong—right about now she'd be having a baby, hard . . . and a thick-set old storekeeper who took his letters said urgently, "Listen—; there's four thousand years of people what's had babies; all of a sudden it ain't going to work, yet? . . . Here, I got some schnapps. Have a drink, we'll wish the baby luck with de mother."

He had a small compact package for the last stop, an undertaker. "Here, hold it in your hands, Uncle Sam, will you? I'll sign the receipt on top of it." The genial man signed behind his cigar. Through a side of the cigar-lips he said as he signed, "Know what you're holding for a writing table?" "What? Cigars?" "An old man from Massachusetts, cremated. His ashes." Down plunked the old man to the floor, out of Joseph's hands. And the cigar man staring at the sudden disappearance of his desk, burst out laughing.

Somehow the calmness of that steadied Joseph. Life and death, how calm and accepted, how matter-of-fact the people between birth and death, carrying on. . . . Under his tilted visor-cap Joseph carried on.

He paced the glowing dim hospital corridor. Down it a man who had spent two days and nights there with only a chair to rest in, sat wearily crying with head in hands; his wife had died in still-birth. A nurse came out smiling from Joseph's lady's door: "You win; it's a girl."

She smiled weakly from the bed, her tired arms stretching out. "For you—" In the wonder of it they clung and cried, laughed and drifted along together. This slim-armed slip of a girl— She was gentle and calm in her sadness. "The one at the end of the hall had a terrible time. She was so strong and robust, too. She tried hard to help the doctors. She put up a fight, for her man in the hall. She lost in the middle of it. The nurses are pretty hard here; but even they felt it. I guess we all did. We all cried. . . . Doodie," she said suddenly, in a great weary calm, "we're always brought through. Do you know it?"

The girl had been born at the precise stroke of midnight. There was a dispute. The house doctor claimed midnight ends a day, therefore it belongs to the day before. And he put down: January 20th. But the head nurse, disputing this, claimed midnight's stroke *begins* a day. And crossing out the 20th she put down the 21st.

They asked Joseph's wife to arbitrate, making her decision the correct one. But she wearily said, "I don't care what day. I want my baby."

Joseph decided on the 21st, which is the day they celebrate.

"What shall we call her?" They must put down a name. The two blinked at this. They had not thought of that. The hospital thought this strange. People usually have the name fought out before the baby's coming. "You name her," urged Joseph. "No, you do," his lady gently said, "it was a girl, just as you wanted."

Joseph thought. Suddenly the Bible pages came up before him. He had formerly hunted through the Bible in quest of those sudden bits of realism, such as Potiphar's wife, and harlotry. He said abruptly, "Ruth." She sighed, her tired face looked away. And in quick dismay he said, "And Eve, for you." She grew to be R. E. The R for womanhood, steady and clean; E for the quick pang of afterthought. And she was a placid contented baby, staying just as you put her, with a far murmur of complacency and a sudden smile.

He could not pay the rent, though. While Eve convalesced at the hospital, worrying, he wrote a story that came to him on a simple theme: a granite-faced policeman who at the end could not run in a bum, because the bum could suddenly do a bit of charity for another man down on his luck. He thought of tearing it up at dawn when it was finished, but instead he mailed it off like the endless others. It brought a check within four days, with a suggestion that he sign it or return it if the terms were not right. On wings of unbelief he ran to the hospital. "Look—! They accepted a story." They paid the rent on time.

It was the turning-point. But who knew it then?

Joseph thought it over. He had sold a story. They had published it as a fact story; "A hobo, a cop, a banana and the law enact a comedy that approaches tragedy." With a drawing of the hunted bum for keynote. Joseph's sensibilities were powerfully moved. The world outside had taken one of his inner images, and made it real—even to drawing a likeness of a creature of his wreathings of mist. It did not in the least resemble the banana-craving derelict of his own mind, and he somehow wished they had not tried to draw him; but it was that they had given him to the world at all, that moved Joseph, his creator.

In his mailman's uniform he went to see the editor of his favorite paper. In the awful jam of deadline time he asked to see the managing editor, woodenly repeating before annoyed inner sentries, "I know he'll talk to me." They told him later it was his simplicity got him through; they wanted to throw him down the elevator shaft.

The old gentleman sat in his glass barricade, and smoked his cigar, listening to Joseph marveling that his story had been published. "I wanted advice from the calmest and steadiest editor I could think of. I came to you. I wanted to know whether I should go on, whether there's a writer in me. I don't know."

"Neither do I." He was kindly; but more, he was calm. He said, "At least, you *have* seen print. You've been published. It may be an indication of something there, or it may have been an accident. But you have been published. That fact is more, far more than ninety-nine out of one hundred who write on and on can ever hope to accomplish. Someone saw something there."

This was sobering. Joseph prepared himself to see an accident rather than something there. But since childhood he had created worlds that longed to have life. That was something. The editor nodded. "Time will tell; we can't. But you asked advice." He smiled. "I'm not the steadiest editor. But I'll answer you. I would say, remember that you sold a story, and keep on writing—without hoping too much for material success. If it's there it must come out. About papers. . . . room can always be found, if you feel that you have it in you. Right now we have no opening in the newsroom. But if you possibly can, get into some other department of a paper, and work up toward the newsroom." And he gave Joseph a note to the promotion department. "Keep in touch with me, if you like."

Joseph knew he wanted to get on a paper, any corner of one. Suddenly he knew that behind all the images and the writing urge was determination. For they had nothing downstairs for him and he quickly made such a speech that they agreed to send him out with a little group already full, selling subscriptions, half cash in advance.

He soon led all the rest in sales made. He kept stopping in at the newsroom, to see if there might be an opening there. They began to know him. Going to work one morning he was surprised to hear the guard of an elevated train call out clearly and loud at a station: "Flatbush Avenoo! Underneath is the line to Coney Island and points south; going north is the approach to Manhattan Bridge. This is the shopping center of Brooklyn, home borough of the City of Greater New York. Please avoid crowding and watch your step." But all life long the people had expected: "Fwawabsh airw—, bly blub ub up. Watcherstep," all perfunctorily mumbled at the corner of the door. Joseph hurried down to the B.R.T. office and a man explained, "It's an elocution and politeness course we're trying out. Instead of mumbling we're asking them to try announcing the station and the important points around." The copy-desk editor agreed there was news in this. He told Joseph to sit at some vacant desk and write it. He did, and the editor read it and grunted, looking up through wooden spectacles at one who had felt the thrill of sitting at a reporter's typewriter. "That's all," he said, "leave it with me."

It appeared on the front page under a double-column comic head. Joseph clipped it and put it down breathlessly before the managing editor, who paused and then said, "Show it to the city editor. Mention the night staff." He smiled. "I see you're working on the paper. Good luck to you."

The city editor looked up, annoyed, from his many telephone instruments. "All rightie," he unexpectedly said, "we'll try some assignments on you, space rates. Call in or look in every afternoon before five o'clock, ask if there's anything in the assignment book for you. Whatever you get, come back here to write it and give it to the night editor. I'll tell him you're on."

A great sunburst flooded Joseph. He thanked the editor and fled. He was, gee—! A reporter.

Days, he sold the paper to new subscribers. Nights, he went on assignments, helping to create it. He felt good all over. This was right up his alley.

But at first they took his stuff and he looked in the paper and did not find it. Not a word of it anywhere, no matter how many times he searched every inch of the many pages. His first write-up had consumed two hours. All about an exciting speech by a man surrounded by torchlights. Joseph had never particularly listened to a politician's spoutings before. After a week of blank writing he was called to the copy desk. "You're beginning to understand the difference between noise and news. Only, don't write a book where a stick or two will tell about the district rally. Stay in tonight and answer the telephones when the district men phone stories in. Jot notes down and write them up. Saturday night is heavy; it's the Sunday paper, you know."

He took down stories and wrote them. Most of them were cut. But the one he loved most was not used at all. It was all about a frankfurter man and a cop and a woman with a charge of poison meat; her son was ill; it all wound up in the station-house—frankfurter cart and all, with the desk officer eating a frankfurter to pass judgment on it. The editor rejected Joseph's story because "you made it shout, 'Read me, I'm funny!' If a thing is funny," he instructed, "it will be funny without you."

During the next week they began to use his stories. But the editor growled, "First you wrote novels about nothing; now you find news and give me telegrams. Write news for what it's worth. When you've told the news the story will automatically stop, and not before."

The ever-barricaded editor paused among his ringing of phones. Then he said, "There's a formula. Ever hear it? It's: Who? What? When? Where? How? and What'll come of it?"

Suddenly they ran a heavy head on one and printed it for more than a column. The editorial commentator used it for his next radio broadcast, a digest of which appeared in the paper. They moved Joseph up from no-star to two- and three-star assignments.

Meanwhile, the circulation-promotion crew was dismissed. Joseph went to report this to the managing editor, but stopped mid-voyage; it would be intrusion. Going down again he tried the advertising department. He explained it all; he wanted to get into the newsroom. They sent him out to get display and classified ads in a district, a staff man on salary. He kept just enough coming in to hold his job, somehow. And at night he went out on assignments.

Suddenly election drew near. It was the time of the Walker Clubs. All Brooklyn was in doubt; nobody knew surely whether Mr. Walker would get any districts in the Democratic junta that was rising against Mayor Hylan. The paper sent him down to a key district where rumors were strong; they seemed unimportant, the district man had been able to substantiate nothing of it.

Joseph was in a fog down there. "Go find out about that meeting of district captains. There's a rumor the assembly district is going to break for Walker tonight." They nearly threw him down the stairs, because when they had refused him admission he had tried to sneak in the back way, and was discovered. He reported his failure. "We expected that. But, will you mosey around anyhow? It would be lovely if we *could* get a line on it somewhere."

That settled it for Joseph. Caesar had need and had sent a messenger, without expecting anything. It stung his pride.

He moseyed around. There was a Walker Club nearby. On impulse he went in and explained the stalemate. They were instantly on the alert. "You want the story?" They cooked a plot. Messengers went out mysteriously and came back with reports. They had found a captain to bribe, a Walker believer at heart, and another to check up on him. The two had left immediately to attend their district meeting. And Joseph flew to the phone. "Fine! All rightie . . . call back. We'll keep a hole in the front page till deadline."

There was a car quietly purring down in the dark of the street, full of secret Walker men and their leader. As the district captains began to stream out of the meeting they saw the one they wanted, going by on his way home. They hauled off and dragged him into the car, which swept quickly away. "Come on, out with it: we'll know if you're stringing us." . . . And Joseph ran panting to the phone, reaching an ear that had given up hope of hearing. "The paper went down,—but what have you got, anyway?" And Joseph panted it out, and even as he began it he heard the city desk snapping: "Hold on! Call down to stop the press—"

They got enough into a hole of the front page of that first city edition to stir all the city. Joseph trembled Monday when he saw in a rival paper a three-column lead head and a column of hot denial that Brooklyn's first district "had swung for Walker." But the city editor told him simply, "You worry when *we* worry. The denial makes your scoop the bigger."

They promoted Joseph to the top assignments. And he covered an international peace or goodwill dinner, the city's nightly freak stories, the sudden comedies and tragedies, the features and the sob stories, and they began to give him assignments with chuckles. "Here's one up your alley." "Look—; they won't see anything in this, but I think you will. Let it mull over and see if there's anything in it." Or, abruptly, "Here—; get right down there quick and—try not to let them know there's a reporter; this rector's slamming his church leaders for a resolution on Prohibition."

And . . . Helen Keller. That grand human triumph of the spirit over the flesh. She could feel the dead pauses and the impulsive bursts of applause though she could not hear her own voice speaking. The managing editor was there, and the commentator-editor. Neither did more than briefly nod to Joseph; no worry or anything. This trust made him feel strong. The story ran half a page in his tense rush of copy. She had moved him. He handed it in fearfully. This was a novel and they had wanted a bit of feature news.

But they ran it for half a page—not a word cut. With comments and photographs.

Joseph had arrived. "You're more than just reporting a thing; you see something there and let it carry you for what it seems worth. It's your own field," commented the Desk. "Go to it."

But Joseph suddenly demanded transfer to the provinces, out on Long Island. God knows why. They stared. The Desk said bluntly, "You're getting there—and now you want the grass. That's a graveyard for newspapermen, out there; what's behind it?"

"I wanted to try the day staff."

The Desk grunted. "You'll wind up waiting till news comes up and hits you in the face. . . . What are you going to do out there—the great American novel?"

The son of the Tired sire said nothing. The editor had said it.

BOOK TWO

Chapter I

THE CHALLENGE

Dust settled, for months, over a heap of papers of futile reporting, some eight thousand in number, that lay in Joseph's attic. They represented a man's effort to explain why he did what he did. He failed to report how his little plan for living blew his house into the ditch, how he came to wander among "boulders, bestrewing the dead sun," or where the convert in him began, or where anything began. But it ended with a swordthrust that flung man and wife apart. But in that ghastly pile, representing two years' effort, he recorded the inner man trying to urge that a straight line be followed, cost what it might.

He failed to explain anything. But in that heap of writing that returned him again and again to page one, and in the snapping of singing nerves that had ended the effort at last, is the testimony of authenticity, the seal of believable truth. Some of these papers, salvaged from the heap, are the basis of the report now opening before you. For they seem to photograph, not a man who was trying to explain to the world, but a man who had tried to be honest with himself. For a thing he had built for his family had suddenly smashed it. And finding himself guilty he tried to trace his way backward to find out how it had happened.

And when he saw that he had gone groping back to birth itself, and that instead of explaining anything he had but written the account of his life, he let it stand for whatever light one man groping may offer to the rest of us.

That is all. That and nothing more.

In the pile of discarded writings, sheets bearing the numeral "Page One" occurred more than one hundred times; that is to say, he broke off nowhere and returned to the beginning of the report at least one hundred times.

In practically every new start, he seems to have begun around the incident of the move from the city-newsroom to the "grass" of a provincial news-area. This is therefore important. He must have felt that the key to all that happened was in the motives or urges or whatever caused him to come to this place where it was all to happen. How hard he tried to analyze the reasons for making such a move!

Reports Joseph, in one of the torn-up efforts, "When I don't know why I am impelled to do a thing, I go ahead and let it do itself. There seems to be no more reason than that."

He thought he had come here to write the books that were in him, three in number, and he did seven years' versions of them before tangling them up beyond another rewrite. "But," he concludes in another start of the report, "I could have done all this in town, as completely as out here. There was leisure enough in the city; it wasn't more writing time, then, that brought me here. And I certainly didn't *long* to leave the city whose jams of people and ashes and smells and heat and mad symphony of clashes and noises I loved, the concourse of people whose very number I love, all running, laughing or muttering to get out of the surprise attack of rain, all crowding back under the drug-store awning to make room for the shrugging young woman backing her spattered crepe shoulders against the human wall, with the crashing curtain of water fringing the sidewalk and spattering her ankles. And I most certainly didn't want a demotion to a provincial post. I suppose the Managing Editor of life itself must answer the question why I was drawn here . . . where all that has happened came crashing down on me. Was it His answer to the filthy dare flung down years before? Did He bide His time, first letting me build myself up so gloriously high before flinging me down to the ground for answer . . . then to pick me again and say quietly in hysteria's echoes, 'Go on'?"

Drawn here. Notice the subconsciousness, pondering.

And, "His answer."

And, "a filthy dare." In lack of explanation for the move he made, here is a bit for speculation, three bits. He mentions that "dare" again and again in the pile of papers.

It had happened long before the move—some time during the bright burst of sun on youth. He thinks it was soon after the Memorial Day parade of the home-coming regiments of France.

Whatever the time, the incident returns in sharp focus, again and again. In it again he can feel the song of that sunburst in his floating stride; and nowhere the slightest feel of a pain or ache or cloud. He felt soaring. He was complete! "Here I am," in wonder he thought, "under the stars; how complete!"

And the stars glimmered down as if to answer back, "Look

—! we light up the night." Light for man in the dark, and a slice of a moon sailing.

He stood still in the sand-lot, to gaze entranced. People with tremendous little minds had measured them, bit by bit down the course of generations, each generation piercing a bit more of the veil, each bit representing the terrific study of an infinitely small mind, and all of them together representing man in his bursting effort to *know*. How beautiful, he wondered, down on the sand-lot, that man could leave off living, to read us the stars! And mealy mouths would set aside this painful search, telling the solemn story of a cabbage baby born to go to a heaven up there.

They would set aside all the glimmer up there, all that universe of worlds that coursed with the speck Earth; they would reduce all that star-sprinkle to Earth's canopy of night; *It* was the world,—it, the puny speck!

"Ah," he burst, "what do *they* know?"

He gazed up again. The sharp-edged boat, the crescent moon, was sailing across the night, with a wake of molten light behind. All the philosophers of his assorted years of reading urged him to see the stars. And man standing under them. All his Roman fathers gazed up with him, and he saw them up there as they had seen them—impersonal, beautiful, majestic,—only gods could be that; and they humbly dedicated names and feasts and powers to them.

Then suddenly he saw that these handfuls of gold and silver dust, sprinkled against black velvet, gave one beautiful thing at least to every heart, his heart's most treasured possession.—And all at once a whole forest of telescopes went poking into this tenderness from every museum roof, while assistant measurers noted down the exact measurement of each star, with a multiple-million-mile jargon and a split-inch fussiness that was sandpaper across all his consciousness.

"Ah, what do *they* know, any better?" he burst out again.

And now he saw Sunday-supplement writers with exotic names all prefixed "Prof." or "Dr.," and all forecasting with pompous importance what life will be like on Venus and the Earth ten million years from now, on the authority of the evolution of ourselves from a single something, through the apes to us, and beyond to a monstrous ant or something, that lives on pills between short visits to a couple of planets, all sketched in life-drawings from the fertile explosion of a peanut mind, which is not sure it shall see tomorrow, much less ten million years.

And ripping these Sunday supplements into shreds in his mind, flinging them down, he walked on down the sand-lot path. Up above, the glimmer of beautiful metals drew him again, and the beauty stabbed him. Then where he had seen a fairy sea to sail the tilted moon, he saw just stars, stars that had first greeted his child heart, through frosty lace on winter windowpanes. Simple friendly stars, that answered back, every night, "You down there yet? Hello, Joey!"

Stars. And he summed up, "There's just that, and us under it." We know something of how they coursed, after thousands of years; but nobody knew *what* they were.

And from whence the immediate exultation sprang, he can never tell. But standing still again he flung up in a burst at the stars, "—You, God! there's nobody there; that's what I think about it; and if you are and don't like it—"

At once he stood stock still, the blasphemous words echoing in the sudden shout in a vacant lot; in a moment's suspension, a feeling that cannot be described waved up over and past him, like warm air, pricking his scalp. It passed and he felt only shame, with awareness of the stupidity of standing in the dark to shout at the sky. And the foul word rested very uneasy on him as he walked away.

It seems not strange, even now, looking back, that he felt not sheepish or ashamed at having brayed at God, even at a mythical God.

In all his boyhood and youth, there simply had been nothing in his consciousness about a God. He had grown up not needing one, and he always knew he did not believe there was any. Now he had professed this belief, out loud. That was all.

It seems he felt a purpose in this: that, being himself freed from the chains of credulity, he must swing the sword to hack the shackles off everybody else—free the whole world. That is why we feel he was quite on the younger side of twenty when he did it. It sounds— But are we trying to excuse him? He went through fatherhood the same unbeliever.

The first mortal he tried to free was his mother, a poor peasant soul who harmed no man, and who prayed for everybody. Her hand groped forth as if to stay the destruction within her son. "Ooh—! you will die, He will abandon you—!"

In strode his father, wrath trembling on his lips. "But when the son must teach the father—" and Joseph went flying backward over the table from the sweep of the back of a hand, "then have we arrived at the *millenio*— Prophet of worms! On your knees, O nothing! and pray the Father Eternal, that He light you the road!"

The sword against credulity stayed dormant thereafter, to break out later in his writing, that unconsciously put anti-Christ into the actions of people. It is remarkable that he never wrote a word with church or worship in it.

It cropped out eternally in the street. Did a man ask fish on Friday, sitting next to him, he must call out, "Meat; what kind have you got?" If God or religion was mentioned, he attacked it.

This did not come out in the months of his engagement, merely because no talk of religion arose. The Luna girl was apparently a Catholic, but her house made no show of religion. He gathered that they were left free to believe as they pleased. When he chose a war chaplain for the marriage, they came to the wedding in the Episcopalian's parlor. He hastens to recall that the Girl, three weeks later at Christmas, urged him to go to a Catholic church. But he demurred, and the couple sat on the doorstep because she longed for the music of Mass. After a while she gave it up, and they drifted away hand-in-hand. That represents Joseph's family history of worship.

At first they had fish on Friday, which he ate to the bone because She cooked it. But gradually he brought meat till no more was said of fish. Herein was life's little ache: a woman was destroying her world, that she might fit into her man's. And the ache was the greater because the man did not see the knife.

He might have glimpsed the flash of it in the mountains, after Gil was born, when she came hesitantly announcing a plan for baptizing their son a Catholic, and he left her standing with mouth open, as if struck in the face. It was not alone that he slashed at her church, but that he cut at it at an hour when she so joyfully pictured her son dedicated by her man to her God. Shamed by her stabbed look, he said, "Any other church; they're all foolish; but if you so want it— Any other church." She said quietly, "It'll be that church or none." And there never was a baptism.

The knife plunged to the hilt at last, five years later in a Brooklyn flat when she was carrying the unborn R. E. It seems he even forgot the incident, for she was to remind him of it on another day. "You said suddenly—I don't remember how we came to talk about it—that there was no God, all your life told you there was no God; you saw my face, and you explained and explained to make it hurt less; but the more you explained, the more it said that there is no God. When you said that," she went on from her convalescent's cot, after the reverberation of the fall of his house had died away, "I wanted to hate you . . . and I was afraid I could."

But he was sweet, kind, brave if mist-locked. Her Man. She went on to remind him that people spoke of his lovable disposition. "You never said a word about anyone that was mean; if you couldn't find a good word you made excuses for him, or kept still. You felt every pain anyone had, you rebelled against tyrants; you ran up to a car full of men and pulled one to the window by the collar to smash his face, because someone there made a remark about me that made me cry; and they all drew back and apologized when any one of them could have wiped up the sidewalk with you, you're so thin. When you stood up for something honest, nobody could stop you. I don't know you now. You're so rotten. The one I knew was so sweet. I don't know where to find him—I've looked and looked—" And the tired eyes in tears clogged up his throat, as they turned away from him on the cot.

Essentially the man who left the city-newsroom to come here in 1926, aged twenty-six, was the one of the preceding book—the son of Tired in a strange bright robe, with a wooden sword strapped beside him, and the sunburst in his face. He knew he was different; he was to do something different; he did not know what, but it was to be something wonderful.

Instead, he came here, established news sources, sat on a stone in the mist and wrote when news rose up to hit him in the face. And seven years whisked themselves away before he got up off that stone, to wander "down a boulder waste," searching for God knows what, except that it wasn't there.

It had not been newspaper work that he sought. This is clear. As a district reporter who must make the daily round, he was a desultory Hans, whose great enthusiasm flared up, grew cold, and left him empty-handed after seven years' apprenticeship to the daily round. But even in that deadness we glimpse Joseph, for one day he found the reporter of his rival paper lying in a hospital, mending broken legs, too English to beg . . . and Joseph for four months sent news every day to the man's paper, that the rival reporter might draw his salary and pay for his legs. This charity was not forgotten. When his paper dropped the Long Island staff, the paper of the Englishman, the same that had disputed his Walker Club item with a three-column blast, picked him up and carried him on, long after he ceased to be a newspaperman, and merely a copy-writer.

Finally he reported a fire on the wrong estate. "Honest, Mrs. T.," wearily called the editor over the telephone, "but for you and the kids I'd have fired him myself, long ago. But it's out of my merciful hands, now." It turned out that the fire had been on the estate of the owner of the paper.

The "merciful hands" part of it rankled most, however. "Ah," he burst, "who asked for his charity?" Forgetting, in the resentment, that he was fired.

"It's like everything else you ever started," said the Tired mother in his wife—"out looking for a job at the end."

"I'm trying to find out where I belong;—if a thing dies out in me it's the only sign that'll tell me that wasn't it."

"And it never will be," wearily.

The urge lasted longest in books.

He wrote day after day, into the night toward dawn, at first with a great glowing urge. His three books drew considerable editorial interest, and sudden praise, but were never accepted for publication. He never knew exactly what was wrong. One was his novel, another was his tenement story with a great first half and a rush for conclusion; the other continues to be a portrait, "A Woman Named Brown" . . .

A small girl with absolutely direct gray eyes would come out of her chatter-and-murmur world, confidently to ask: "Is you sold some book yet?"

There was to be a stone house, rambling over roses, whose breath was to cool the window-seat, where the Luna girl was to rest in matron composure at last, with Keats and Shelley . . . and a private academy for Gil. And a white pony for R. E. out of that "great amazing urge," was to transport the sun-world to Joseph's wreathing mists.

And startled out of that by her directness, he would answer in the instant candor that she demanded, "Not yet. I have to keep changing it because it doesn't come right." "Well, you better hurry up because I need my pony. And a stove with pots on it."

Then he would sit adrift with an ache in his heart. This was his last believer. The Luna girl had jumped to the mailbox too many times . . . and heard the weary editor over the telephone too often . . . or was it that Joseph's plan for living had stilled her?

Joseph's plan for living.

While evolving this beautiful world in the roses, something had happened to the man building the imagery of it. Images got crossed. All his worlds had been pervaded with the wonder of the image of womanhood, in some form or other. Somehow the form got confused. It came out a Jekyll-Hyde affair. It is absolutely too muddled to explain. Now it was womanhood and now it was the marble Aphrodite, beautiful and rotten.

Joseph himself was evolving, that was why, and was sometimes one and sometimes the other, when he should have been a district reporter making a living for a family. But which of us has commanded life to come clear?

His thoughts evolved something like this:

He had no God. He was freed because he stood on the proposition that intellect (sic) teaches freedom from darkness. Find the facts, it said; demand proof; back down myths, release earthy fact. See how they delude themselves with Santa Clauses:

Outliving past worlds of myths, Joseph was suspicious of all these superimpositions across the credulity of man. He had seen his worlds tumbled down too many times by the gleam of clear sun on prosaic fact. As a reporter he reported man, cutter of man's throat in the race to be first. But Joseph wanted to see just men, men in the street, men and women trying to get through the world, each with his opinion of it, and all getting along together, somehow, at the same baseball game, under the same sudden rainstorm, around the same dead face in the parlor, and at the same pay-booth in the subway glow, all the human family groping along from woman's breast, to what?

"We're one," he concluded; "we don't know what it's all about but any one of us will stick his suitcase or her fur coat under my head if I slip and crack it."

What Joseph felt, but had no name for, was the family we all belong to . . . proving our kinship in sudden ways . . . and searching for What, everyone for himself.

"Everyone has a right to search for it," he told his wife. "We need it to make us go on at all. One man longs for a farm, another man needs an apartment and night life. This one finds joy in beautiful clothes and eyes that look back at him; a can of beer is enough for this other one. It's a sniff of cocaine for someone else; sex fills it for this other one. But no matter what it is, somebody who finds it some other way or gets burned trying it your way gets up and tells you it's all wrong. But everyone has a right to live it out his own way."

This grew suddenly into the life-plan.

"I'm freeing us both. Life is however you see it. Whatever in life can make it more endurable, whatever fills *your* need best, is a thing that only you need to decide. No matter what it may be, if it seems to you that it will add to the moment's peace or make life in any way more endurable, you have a right to it,—and all the must-nots can't make it wrong." He added after a pause, "I said no limit, but there *is* a limit. If something you want, in any way cuts into the peace of the next man, right there you give up your right to it. Live your life according to whatever makes life livable; but take nothing, do nothing that can harm anyone but yourself. I'd say that's the one commandment of this freedom."

And he built his house on this plan.

Chapter II

FLOODED PASSAGE

In all life there is no spectacle more painful than the host who is saved when his boat full of friends goes down. There he stands in the pool of his own dripping clothes with the startled faces of his friends seared on his mind. Hysteria is just behind the huddle of his words, as he explains over and over, over and over, to whoever will hear, how strong the boat looked in its new paint, how he shined each brass and rail; and how the bottom was rotten, the bottom was so rotten. But he didn't know, nobody told him; and the pallor and silence of his wife's face was fixed on his with the huddle about her, just before this huddle was swallowed, clinging to the rails. He didn't know; the flags fluttered so surely in the breeze. But the guests lie at the bottom of the sea. He had even forgotten the lifeboat, which was so brightly painted.

Joseph had launched a life-plan. He did not know at first about its rotten bottom.

It is impossible to trace back the beginning of its construction. A launching is but the completion. Joseph might perhaps have named his vessel: *Self*. He had released it.

It was the age of "self-expression." It may have influenced him. It is more probable that he did not so much set free a *self,* as that he surrendered to lust, which needed "freedom" to justify it.

Perhaps there can be no harm in reporting one result of his plan for freedom, that touches only Joseph. He wrote a filthy book. There is absolutely no other word for it. It wrote itself from the sweep of that fire which he had never learned to keep banked.

He wrote it in privacy at first, but later quite openly. It was finished and bound in oilcloth at last, some five hundred pages deep, profusely illustrated with good-enough pen sketches of the freedom he wished to represent. And they were more revolting than the words.

While deep in the surge of the writing of the thing—and a wife's silence is its own contempt after a lashing of words—he looked up to find Mill there, one of his strongest believers, and unshakably an ear. Some people are backs, some hands, some fists, or sneers, or a cheer. She functioned as critic. Calm, flung down enough by life's blows, and steady in the moment of panic, she always outlives it. She had wandered in for a smoke and some word to hear about his books.

"What's this?" she murmured, picking up some sheets; "a new one?"

He hesitated, and—showed it all.

But she did not hesitate to sum up, with her imperturbability, "If this is intellect freed, something cracked to let it out."

Long after she had gone, he sat there. She had casually stepped in, led him out from within and had said, "This has become you, this mud."

There was something which weighed Joseph down. Papers cluttered the table—he wrote in the dining room. But he was not writing. He was as he had been all through two weeks—motionless and still. He could not bear to release the writing flow, for fear of releasing the filthy book again, whose last pages needed revising. Mill had shaken him. There was always something behind her calm that he respected. A kind of judge.

Seeing through her imperturbability, he saw himself and wanted to beg the mud to leave him. He had written an elaborate monument to slime.

R. E. had come wandering up with a doll hanging by its hand, all candor in her face, gazing from the silenced typewriter to his face, which tried to come alive for her.

"Yes, Princess—?"

"Why don't you write the book to sell?"

It stung. "Maybe I'll try again—for you."

She accepted this with the readiness of six, gone cynical. "I guess I s'pose I'll be too old for a pony, when you sell one."

She wandered away with her doll. He sat there, motionless, as if longing to find her confidently at his elbow again. She had been his last believer.

He drifted down to the *Echo*. He was at home here. Nobody asked questions that left him silenced. They walked around him. They did not know he had written a dirty book.

He felt a cracked laugh within. The goddess Lust lived in there. He had set her on a pedestal. But he thought he had freed himself.

Time hung heavy. He sat at the young secretary's desk.

She did not need it. She was cleanly kneeling before dusty files, rearranging them. He sank a-sea into himself . . . and was cramped over the desk, scribbling a sequence of the book of mud.

It was closing time. They were getting ready to go home. . . . He picked up his paper.

Next morning, sane in the sun, he walked into the *Echo*. His friend the editor turned sharply around beside the desk, at sound of the cheery "Good-morning." He did not return it. He was whistling under his breath—five or six notes in a jumble.

Joseph was taken amidship. Then across the desk the old man pushed three sheets of scribbled copy-paper toward Joseph, the sheets of filth of last night. He had forgotten to pick them up.

The floor refused to open under him.

"You'll have to make other arrangements; you left this stuff on the desk," suddenly said the editor, "my young woman found them this morning. I can't have you in here, leaving stuff like this around for my bookkeeper to find; it turned her sick; I can't have my people upset. It's a good thing you weren't around, when she came up shaken to me—"

He was whistling again, not listening to Joseph explaining that he had found a piece of dirty writing, and had set about showing the writer how dirty to write, if that was the aim. How we will cover self's nakedness! What Joseph really meant to say was said by a hand that groped forth halfway to the old man: "Don't condemn all of me—there's one side really clean in me, trustworthy, with a sword to swing; *he's* not guilty." And babbled something burning-cheeked instead, a lie, about a piece of writing he had *found*—

Echo John swung around again. "I can't understand an intelligent man lowering himself to write that stuff; you can't do it in here, that's all. Get out."

He stood still, at last. He had run and stumbled from the other rim of the world, into, at last, this desert of dead sun bestrewn with boulders. They stretched to nowhere in every direction. He was conscious of the echo of tears. He had cried. Cried of too much self.

No matter how far, he found he could not run away from himself. He sat against a boulder, drew up his knees in the clasp of his hands, and gave up trying to run from self.

He tried to think. But he knew only how to make images in mist. He knew only how to feel. And now he had run from reaction.

He tried again. It hurt his head. He wanted to cry instead. He felt very sick and sorry for the man within. In there was the clean, really fine one who was trustworthy. And he had led this spirit into a long sewer to live. His plan had burst.

He went home with a story of a confirmation class in the Episcopal Church that was to start tomorrow, for Gil and R. E. and later for himself; would she try?

She stopped dusting about. He explained, then, that he had been thinking about the children, pagans, without a goal to keep them from being empty like himself. Then he saw her face of indifference as she resumed dusting. "Heat strike you, or what?" she said.

Joseph came to. "It *is* sudden."

"You must be cracked."

"It doesn't look like you're tickled, much," said Joseph. "I thought you'd—"

"I'd what—jump up glad all over? I got all over that with you, long ago. What—you all of a sudden having another experiment, and the whole world has to stop and change over with you? I've got over even listening."

He was absolutely stopped dead. Here he had thought he was doing a tremendous thing—making himself over; an atheist willing to think of church for his children—

"I admit," he said, burning with the justice of her response, "that I'm a prophet of nothing; my father was the first to tell me. But for once in my life I'm thinking of something other than myself,—of church for our children. And it doesn't mean a thing to you."

She said quickly. "I *am* glad—"

Then she went on, nor could he mistake the tiredness of years, "No mother is glad, seeing her children growing up without God. It *is* something, coming from you. . . . What made you think of it?"

He did not know. "I suddenly looked backward. Or the desert I saw myself in. Or the mud. I don't know. Everything I touch turns to water. The dead books. I don't know what." She saw the troubled mind trying to know why.

"What do you want us to do, now?" quietly.

He felt sudden mud. "*I* don't want anybody to do anything—I'd lead you into a sewer again. . . . I got thinking about the kids, all of a sudden. I didn't want them like me. I'm— What right has a father got to see for his sons? They have a right to see for themselves. I thought I was freeing them from myths; they were to climb up on my shoulders and climb up. No Santa Claus. Calmness. They burned me plenty when I was a kid. But suppose *they* can see a God?" he argued in sudden earnestness again, from the boulder desert. "I don't see any; I'm what I am; that's all settled. But teaching them there's no God I'm selling them my emptiness. Telling them there's just this and the worms in the grave I may be doing them the worst damage any father can do his children, instead of freeing them."

"Oh," their mother shrugged, "you *can* see that? I gave up hoping. You've been so sure there is no God; you've attacked Him enough."

"Well, I haven't changed my mind—get *that* straight," snapped Joseph; "if you think so you're crazy; I'm thinking of the children. I'm still a father;—if *they* can see a God I'd be gladder than you;—by Jesus, I know what it is to be full of just my wonderful intellect—it makes me so free I could scream of emptiness: do you think I'm tickled about it, unable to accept anything higher than myself? But what my mind will accept it will accept; what I am I am—and I don't feel glad about it; but I don't feel like apologizing, either." He saw that he was not calm and he calmed himself; she had heard enough of his speeches. "*I* don't know how I came to think of a church for them—and us; I've had rottener ideas—"

Her hand started toward him; she let it sink down at her side. Quietly she said, "You don't know how glad I am, I never expected ever to—" She wiped the table again where she had already wiped. Then as if it seemed better to talk in a matter-of-fact way she asked, "What made you think of Doc T.'s church?— I mean, did it have to be his church, especially?"

"Well—no, it didn't; no special reason. I suppose it's because he's like Doc A. down at the other village—a man with whom I can talk business, books, life, Prohibition, trouble—whatever comes up in the news or the talk of two who don't intrude, just look at each other's views. I could trust him with our kids, I thought. . . . Also, it's a church I wouldn't have to make excuses for; it's plain and solid; the people who talk my language go there. It doesn't make any difference what church, though," he summed up.

"Then why not the Catholic Church?"

"That—?" Then he savagely burst. As ever, as ever. The words are forgotten. Priests and monks and bells and a rigmarole lit up like a theatre, "all crammed down the throat with a holy-holy attitude that makes me want to tear the mask off, a fake—; if it takes all that to hold poor ignorants in line, with a threat of hell for trying to break loose from it, they haven't got any God to sell—; if you can't find this God in a quiet church where you can read or sing or just sit and try to feel your way to a God it proves what I have always said: that there isn't any God to find, anywhere;—and if the Catholic Church were the only place where a God could be found, sooner than submit to the stuff that filled my whole boyhood with a pretty glow and superstition and a slap in the face by a priest," he ripped out, "I don't want any part of it for my kids, if I have to burn in hell for it.—Is that plain?"

She shrugged. "It's plain enough that you hate the Catholic Church; I could recite that all by heart, I've heard it so often."

It was true. A hymn of hate— And this was the Catholic he had stilled, the girl who had builded on him.

He drifted off and stood staring woodenly at the past; he could not sit on a lunchwagon stool on Friday beside a man ordering fish without calling out, "Beef, for mine." Hate. He stared down through the reaction of it at village traffic crawling in the street. Hate was anything but intellect. . . . Drifting back, he did not know how to tell her these things that he felt. He couldn't face her clean convalescent pallor, with his whiplash across it.

Then he saw that she stood where he had left her. She glanced up.

Her face was gentle.

"Did you want me to try it with you?"

"I thought—" he looked at the mother of his children. "Forget it," he murmured.

But she said quietly, "I'll go with you."

They found Doctor T. in the chapel, behind the parish hall, herding three rows of little children.

The small faces looked up with blinks of wonder at two adults sitting among them—tow-haired boys and clean little girls with eyes so limpid and innocent. Joseph felt a stranger among them; all that was clean in him longed to be horsewhipped.

The rector came over, trying to find, as he came, the right casual offhandedness.

"Mrs. T. I'm very glad. This is Gil?" He smoothed the dark head of a small dreamer. "Think you'll try two schools, eh?" Gil guessed so. He chucked the chin of the casual little girl swinging her long pink legs from the pew. "And who is this young lady?"

"Ruth Eve T.," promptly replied R. E.; "I live down the same block. Do you give stars?" There would be stars for good pupils, she was assured.

The white-headed rector had not expected the adults. He covered the awkwardness gracefully. "We're just forming the class; I won't ask my two oldest pupils to sit through recitations, I think. There are a few things to know, that can be explained toward the end, things about our form, and what God really is,—just the essentials I believe we ought to know. I'll let you know when. Meanwhile, study this." To each he gave a prayer-book, and into Joseph's hand a limp leather book—through which furtiveness had hunted in search of mud. "Do your best with it," abruptly said the minister, as wooden fingers closed on the small Bible.

He did his best with it. He sweated over it.

He read the small print till his eyes swam, late into the night. He read with painful slowness, with such an earnestness as he had never known. "And—my God," he writes in a passage of the report, "a rebel wanted to snarl at any part of me that might prepare to challenge one word of it."

Here is intensity itself, telling about it in the salvaged sequence: "My mind was co-operating—gently, gently—helping me over the difficult parts, the whale and the divided river and the eight centuries of a man's life—even turning around to find itself ahead of me and waiting gently, it seemed, for the rest of me to understand the passage, take my time, and catch up with the mind, as if to say, 'No hurry, take all the time needed; I know it's a lump to swallow whole; but look—I accepted it just as it is, I, your ever-snarling rejecting mind.' It is unexplainable—and, let me freely say, unbelievable. But it is the exact truth. My mind accepted instantly while the senses reacted; then the mind gently stood by to prepare for an assault of unbelief which never came.

"The senses co-operated with the mind. There were times of such slow digging, such laborious re-reading of a passage whose import I feared to miss, that I *felt* this partnership of mind and consciousness—or with consciousness and *something else,* some stranger acting as guide, perhaps? But I felt a very gentle urge as if at my mind's or senses' elbow—bidding me to read the passage steadily over just once more—and to go on from there, understanding it if I could: and if I could not grasp it, bidding me to accept it *just as it was, on the authority of the passage itself.* And I accepted it as the word of God."

He gives us the outcome, his absolute acceptance of the Old Testament:

"I longed to feel Jehovah, repenting that He had made us; I wanted him to possess me, move me, fill me; I wanted to rage with the flood, conquer with the cloud of the tabernacle, move with the mountain, split with the waters, and be filled with the rain of manna. And I did! I groaned with us all when we went the other way and Moses smashed the road signs; I wanted to cry out, 'Try us again, Moses!' I wanted Jehovah to possess me body and soul. I went to the Confirmation service with the class of children, we marched slowly in behind them, my wife beside me in her pallor but with a gay scarf; we shuffled in behind the column of children who followed the cross, over the threshold of the church into the rumble and tremor of the organ depths, into the glow over people in the pews, toward the face of the Bishop behind the last of the children, and into the oil which anointed me to make a Christian of a Roman pagan. Then trembling because I felt no different and unmoved, I sought for Jehovah again in the pew amid kindly gazes beside my silent Lady, and found only a great disturbance; I tried to feel God again within me in the Bible of sweated reading and bursting acceptance—and found myself walking out of a church of Christ absolutely as empty as before seeking the Rector from the desert of the boulders. And my whole world trembled.

"I could so unexplainably accept the Book of God—but going to a church raised to Him I found myself the atheist of before.

"It was years later before I discovered what I had attempted to do: I had accepted the Old Testament but had read not a word of the New; I had felt absolutely no need to inquire into the New Testament which to me seemed inappropriate to a search for God. I had rejected as not needed the Testament of the Son of God—yet I proposed to approach, and did approach, confirmation as a *Christ*-man, a Christian, a follower of this Son of God, in a church raised to this same Christ whom I had not needed.

"And the paradox amazed me. And in later calm I wondered: Was it that Christ in His plan for me had called me but had seen fit not to reveal Himself to me yet—by shutting me away from His Testament?"

But then, Joseph has ever been one to propose unanswerable questions.

The passing over was not a total disaster. Joseph and his wife failed to gain the far shore; but the children went on, hand in hand to Sunday school and church. Had Joseph so much as suggested that they be taken out of a place so crushing to his search, she would have snarled back at him. They were finding the road.

Twice Joseph went with her to Sunday services among the people, and took wine in the glass of the sacrament, and he knew not what it signified, so that it was utterly wasted. Then toward spring his wife burst out suddenly, "Take me away from this village—I can't stand it."

They moved back to Glen Cove.

There was the Episcopal church of Doctor A. in an adjoining village. To him went Joseph, explaining, without preliminary, the failure and the children.

Then, going on, "I wanted to turn the children over to you, if you don't mind their coming from an atheist—a confirmed one."

"I'd be glad of the trust."

"I'll bring them Sunday." Joseph struggled with an impulse.

"Doc, I have a question. I want you to answer it straight out from the man inside—I don't want the church answer, but the other one; I don't know how to put it and I know it's an insult." He stopped, troubled. "What right have I, putting you on the spot?"

"Ask it," quietly, "I understand what you mean."

Joseph protested with a shake of his head; they stood in the sun in the street. "It's that damned wanting-to-know-absolutely, driving me; I have to rip at the inside of a man as if suspecting him. . . . The answer is going to mean everything to me, Doctor—the answer may not be the one I want, but it's got to come straight from within you; it's the only way it can help me." He felt hot all over. The rector was absolutely calm.

"What is the question?"

"When you pray or in any way face God, do you feel that you're speaking with a definite being—as if with a man?—with someone tangible? Do you feel Him there? Can you honestly say, that you *believe* you are talking to a listener?—I'll think just the same of you whichever way you answer, Doc," pleaded the damned fool; "do you honestly feel Him there?"

"Yes—I can feel Him there when I talk to Him." He was very pale; was he longing to smash him in the face? But he was quiet and steady and he repeated, "Yes—I can say that; when I talk to Him I feel that He is there."

For some reason an immeasurable weight fell from Joseph. At the same time the indefensible thing he had done grew on him. He said simply, "Doctor, you've helped me more than you think—more than I, possibly, can realize; a load has left me, it's the only sign I can go by." He added quietly enough after a pause, "I can trust my children to you, Doctor. Fill them with that same God, if you can. I'm going to try to feel Him too;—it's a job," he said with what must have proved a weak enough smile, "my mind rejecting it all. But if I fail, what's lost? . . . Doc, pray for me, the odds are heavy against me." Quickly pressing the man's hand, he left him standing there.

Nothing came of the effort to feel out God. In the end he gave it up. He went to the church on Sundays to gather up the children and take them home, the unbaptized children confirmed Christian, who were trying Sunday school. Rain or blow or a hangover from an empty man's effort at a gin party the night before, or what, he saw the children to and from school. But, for him the experiment had failed.

Once when the children had sore throats, the Rector anxiously telephoned; and Joseph found that he was somehow *glad* that there was an authoritative Churchman in the picture —glad that someone in authority cared whether Joseph's children attended God's class or not. Yet Joseph was himself unable to see a God.

There seemed nothing left for such a man to do but to get the war-veterans' families together now and then for parties of drinking and noise. It helped to submerge the memory of a freedom.

It is perhaps explainable. Joseph's world had fallen; empty, he still carried on in the ruins.

He worked in the weekly-news shop of the small town. He had dropped out of the world of city editors. For Joseph it was the absolute end of the newspaper lane. He felt it horribly. The great bursting urge born on night assignments had died. He was gathering local paragraphs now—with an occasional rebellion in the editorial column or a strip of desultory comment on life. But life itself seemed to have died. There was no image to move him.

It was 1932. A world depression had reached its peak in the United States. He wrote two editorials that are memorable. They give such a glimpse into Hans-in-Luck that it seems a pity he did not save them. One was on Mother's Day. It was written when loneliness must have gnawed at him. He scattered us in the ports, the brothels and the missions; mislaid, stranded, carousing or trying to patch people up; and he crossed the abyss of seas to depict hope worn thin in the form of Mother, wondering where Jim or Mary can be, while wrinkled old lips try to pray . . . and he pictured the shabby remembrance that we hastily express in the form of a box of roses, and then he damned it all. He made the tired-out hope jump up at sound of a quick step in the door and a haggard face bursting eagerly through, behind harlot paint or beachcomber's bristles: he showed not the army of sons and daughters coming home to say hello to her, but a haggard wreck in a skirt or sour whites . . . who at some far port had run with a sob after some rusty steamer blowing its clear-away siren.

He seems to have said in that: we don't think of the old doorstep till we're down on the rocks somewhere; but mother wants you back, she doesn't care in what condition you come, just so you come.

Amen, Joseph! . . . The other editorial he never hung on the linotyper's hook. It was a sudden clear call of encouragement, such as might have rung out from some shell-hole from a stranger who sees you beaten slowly down by too many bayonets, and who wants your sinking senses to know that help is coming.

The editorial was to have shouted out to discouraged Americans losing the battle with Depression: "Hang on—! don't let go!"

Then he himself let go his own grip and receded . . . to shuffle up and take his place on the breadline, having quit his last job.

Had he written that editorial for himself, feeling his grip failing?

Chapter III

ON THE RELIEF ROLLS

The thing that he did resists analysis. When millions had no employment and had to be fed by the others, this family head must quit his job and throw his house upon the mercy of that hastily built structure, Relief.

Yet few men have been more eager to work. And few have needed to put their noses to the grindstone more unconditionally. For he had betrayed the family that must follow him. His wife had hardly completed her convalescence when she was rushed to the little door of life-or-death again for an operation. Out of something pursuing her in the hour of crisis, she had burst out in agony, "No, no—! no, no, no, no—I love *him*, I *love* him!" and sat bolt upright to seek him everywhere, as if despairing of where to find him. Slim arms fumbled up to find him, when the crisis had spent itself. And she would not let him go. And he must force a woman like this to eat relief bread.

He went home with senses upset. It is no calming thing, to quit a last job and throw a house upon the charity of a village. He knew he would not find work; desperate men and women looked everywhere . . . and went to the breadline, or found unbearable other ways.

"There was no more money to pay the wages," he told his wife. Could he speak of revolt?

Friends in town hurriedly sent money, and letters to friends and editors. One letter brought an assignment . . . that failed. But while searching about town for the unreportable assignment, he found in a newspaper the First Century Christian Fellowship. Religious leaders breaking away from sect had established a back-to-the-beginning movement, a brotherhood based on the guidance of Christ.

Joseph's heart leaped. Here was the torch, lying sputtering on the ground!

He put it down before the editor of the wasted assignment. "It's been written to death," it was just another movement in a world of movements and countermovements. Joseph was dashed. He had failed to keep in touch with the times, the world had gone moving on without him. But it was still his torch!

He said abruptly, "All right, it's been done to death. But it's what I was looking for."

First Joseph wanted to be sure. Another disillusionment would kill all further search for Something in him—and he knew it. He must not make a mistake this time. He began to talk to men and women in the street, on trains, in gathering places. He wanted to know how the man-in-the-street reacts to a go-back-to-the-first-century Christianity. He wanted to be filled and must not make a second mistake.

He was bound to fail. Ideals are not nourished in the street, but in the heart. The street levels them down to a common denominator. The denominator is earthy, of the earth. Ideals are revolt and protest, urge and a longing to see a thing grow in our hearts. The street is right. It learns with a fist in the face. The street itself is the greatest idealist. It picks itself up and goes on, living its ideal of all life: pick up your cross and carry it.

He put his question. The street's realists, carrying God knows how many ideals gone bruised and hacked and soured, mostly looked at Joseph and walked away. One of those religious crackpots. If he had some tract or paper to give out with his brisk query, they would obediently have taken one and dropped it after a few steps. On the street they take whatever you offer. The street is resigned to accept chewing gum, samples of sawdust cereal, dentist advice, a theatre bill, a Communist paper. If there is a soapbox and two or three musical instruments for fanfare, an audience will hear you. Lacking these credentials, you are left there with mouth open. One lady took him for a flirt. A man with a stepladder grinned obediently and shambled away. A citizen nervously sidetracked him, possibly with fear that his pocket might be picked. But a heavy-set man with a red Irish face stopped to turn out to be an argumentative Jew, taking his cigar out of his mouth to say, without malice:

"How do I react, to this first-century Christian movement? All right; I'm a Jew. I'll ask one back: Why not back to Confucius? Or Egypt? Or the Holy Rollers? I could say, how about Abraham? But what's the good of an argument? I'm wasting time." He put his cigar back in his mouth and walked away.

A minister was on the train going home, a young man sitting pallidly alone, against the window. His look as he heard the query was absolutely cold. "I know where to go for my religion." "I'll try not to steal you from it," Joseph cut at him, and walked back to his seat. The coldness of the churchman had stung him when he expected bread.

Going to town next morning on the train he saw a heavy-set and rather rusty cleric who might be of the Episcopal form, for he had some of Dr. A.'s complacent composure, an air of feeling secure. Joseph went to sit by him.

"Please accept me as an inquiring reporter, not trying to stir up a rise: I suppose you've followed the First Century Christian Fellowship?" The rector calmly nodded. "Somewhat." "How do you react? I see a search for the beginning, away from sect; I realize I'm speaking to the cloth; but I'd be glad to have your opinion on the movement, how it strikes you."

"I'd say, it looks in the right direction; we seem to have drifted a long way from the beginning. But you mention a search. Why seek? You'll find the spirit of the first century right where it has been all these ages, intact: in the Roman Catholic Church, that carries it forward through the ages; it's exactly today what was deposited in trust centuries ago."

Joseph rather hurriedly went back to his seat, away from this priest, representative of the church he hated most. The man had been calm, sure, and therefore, to Joseph, presumptuous. Had he guessed it would be a priest, he would have sat where he was. "He was sure enough," he muttered.

Giving up all further inquiry in the street, he went to the central library in town. For it struck him that he knew nothing about Christ, or Christianity. He had read of, on, about, over, and under it, but never Christianity itself. He despised the imposed credulity of it, and the hypocrisy of Christendom.

He searched the index and moved up one wall and down the other, looking for books with which to make a start, a slippered atttendant shuffling patiently beside him. At last he found exactly the title he wanted, leaping right out at him.

He read all day till lights shone out in the darkness, and eyes swam. Then, wandering about, he waited till nearly eight o'clock and went down Broadway to the dry-goods district, to search out the place where the Fellowship was.

It was in a building on Episcopal Church property. To a young-enough man of few and frugal words he stated his reportorial assignment, and was coldly received. Reports had been misrepresentative and magazine articles garbled; what was Joseph's motive? Joseph stated it: to earn money for bread, being unemployed, and to know more about—

"I'll make it definite at once," the official broke in, "that we discourage any idea of a hand-out; the people that come here come for better than that." Joseph was upset. "We're not interested in what people think they need, we're not a job agency nor a food kitchen."

Joseph had a longing to smash him in the face.

"You needn't worry about what kind of publicity you'd get in a story," he said; "I've not started to twist a story yet, for any man. . . . And I can manage my own food hand-out. Get *that* straight."

"You can stay and see what the meeting is like," the man suggested.

Joseph saw men and women beginning to come in and go upstairs. They were extremely complacent, well-dressed, and on obviously secure ground here; they called one another by their Christian names. The absolute matter-of-factness and the use of first names appealed to Joseph standing apart in the lobby. Here seemed Christian steadiness, Christian smiles.

The meeting was informal. The people sat in chairs drawn intimately together in a casual semicircle. Here sat Joseph's official, with another man. The atmosphere was extremely pleasant.

The man of the interview called the meeting to order, then he asked a minute's silence, in which Joseph understood he was to meditate on the spirit. The silence passed and the leader called for examples of guidance. Joseph took this to mean, the guidance of Christ. He felt tense. He wanted this. This was simple, it was calm, it dwelled on a founder-Christ, who contacted and gave guidance. No more sects! A concourse of brethren sitting in calmness to exchange examples of guidance, and to open a spiritual meeting.

A young woman stood up, somewhat timidly, to report a job which she had not taken because it had seemed inadvisable after some contact with the spirit at the guidance hour. She spoke overlong on the little she had to give, for the leader perfunctorily assured her that she had done well. Then he asked for other examples, which were more or less of the same order, none of any importance to the intent and perhaps over-eager inquirer in Joseph, who began to understand that guidance urged people to calmness and gave some idea of what to do or not to do. It seemed to him good.

He listened to several, until he longed to express himself, let them see how steady, how calm they were, how comely the Christian face. Just then the leader began to urge more sharply defined examples, he was sure there must be someone present who had a real report to make, some moving example to give—and Joseph fairly had to restrain himself to keep from standing up earnestly to tell how he longed to flow with the spirit their pleasant faces reflected. "Come, come, I'm sure that someone among us is waiting to speak, someone not heard from before, with an experience that went deep—" Joseph felt his flesh creep with his longing to say something . . . but a man rose up just then, a smoothly small and heavy-set individual with a voice too much like a bray, too ringing, too full of Billy Sunday to save Joseph from dismay. For the man was introduced as "our old standby," presumably a repeater with one story to tell, and that loudly, all about how he was saved, many years ago.

Now it was Joseph's distinct impression that any man saved is a man who is silent about it, and that a testimonial is the exact opposite of testimony. He went home unwilling to let the sawdust speaker spoil his suddenly sweet reaction, and he managed to discount the man as an over-zealous convert.

He attended the next meeting, also at night, and fell in with a stranger whose humble dress and obvious newness of manner at once attracted the equally new Joseph. The man was scraggly-tall, with a sparse moustache, country face and gulpy throat, who seemed lonely there. He was from New Jersey, he was a man of the soil. To him the news-cynic and atheist in Joseph were strangely drawn. The two went up and sat together, a little early. "It's great," shyly confided the man, "this is how to do, all git together. It's what I looked for. It's my first time. I—I want to git into the first spirit, that we growed off'n. I hope . . ." He let the rest go unvoiced . . . and Joseph found in him his own great fear of not being moved as he longed to be moved.

It so turned out. Joseph wanted to see first-century feeling, something to light a face, subdue self, and *offer* all that to a universal being. He found just a group of people looking up quickly at each new speaker, to sink back after hearing another trifle reported concerning guidance—nothing deep. He saw doubt cross the scrawny face of the man from New Jersey . . . and he got up and left the meeting, lit a cigarette in the street and flung the match bitterly down. "I knew it!"

There was nothing there for Joseph. But he had looked for a sputtering torch that would be picked up eagerly and . . . was left cold, uneasy, futile, and angry with himself. He tried to give the movement full credit, perhaps he had sought the unfindable, a *spirit*. He had wanted *to be moved.* They had failed him.

Crossing dark Union Square he slid into a bench, unaware of the young woman till she got up, earnestly spoke to a man strolling by, was jolted coldly in the side by his elbow, and sank back sullenly into her seat on the bench, to cross her knees and recede into the back of the seat with profile sunk within herself. She was smooth of dress and well groomed of appearance; but the sole of the shoe she restlessly swung had a hole in it. And her clear skin had a fragile shadow under the eyes. She glanced up to meet Joseph's glance, and ignored it. He looked away and sank within himself. Going to ask food or lodging at the place which he had left, she would have found scanty welcome, he thought. She had a wedding ring. Someone was in need or had kicked her out. The sullenness had gone. She looked weary and had probably forgotten the elbow in her side. "The man needn't have been so rough," he muttered to himself. She heard it. She looked up curiously, with amazingly beautiful eyes set wide in a calm face. "What did you expect him to give me —a pat on the back?"

Joseph looked away. "I came damn' near shoving my foot out to trip him," he said.

There came a seedy elderly man, briskly moving down the row of sidewalk benches, thrusting papers into laps or hands, a quick word went with each. He progressed to the bench of the woman and Joseph. "Read the Word, sister, and be saved . . . read the Word, brother, and be saved." Joseph found a paper tucked into his hand, the girl brushed hers off her lap.

"How will I be saved?"

The tract man turned sharply on Joseph. "You can read, can't you? One o' them wise ones, eh? What 'o you want, an argument?"

Now, this was totally unexpected. He was a religious man; Joseph had no patience left for such now. "I asked a civil question," he snapped; "you've got nerve, sticking your papers into people's laps, and getting anything but humble about it."

"You didn't ask no question, you! I'm onto you wise ones; if you don't want the tract you could drop it."

"It happens I *am* asking;—but all I get is a lot of sauce; if you people expect to get any listeners, this way—"

"No, not from you;—Jesus would be wasted on your kind, trying to talk to you—"

"Well, I'll tell you one thing He wouldn't do," flashed the man who had twice tried, "He wouldn't send out bums to stuff papers into a man or woman's hand—He'd drop them in the first waste can and sit down and talk, find out what's the trouble, tell someone up against it to try again—"

"*You* know Him so good," broke in the man; he glared; "you wan' 'o read the Bible; I'd like to know where you get your idea of Him from."

"From your Bible," the young woman broke in.

When the man went his way, the man seated beside Joseph let the paper in his hand fall away, saying in Broadway calm, "Best thing is to take their paper and let them go; it's the easiest way; nobody pays any attention."

Joseph composed himself to read the tract in his hand. It was full of brimstone and damnation, in phrases that hurled such a roasting, crackling assurance of eternal agony to those who did not at once seek Jesus, that Joseph crumpled the evil composition into a ball and flung it down.

"That's just exactly the way to drive a man away from Him," he muttered, "fling a lot of slogans and threats like this at him—why, you'd never reach the emptiest man with this in a thousand years—and it happens I *wanted* to be reached."

"They don't get many." The man beside Joseph shrugged and gave himself up to his calm boredom . . . and Joseph presently got up and drifted away, smouldering less, empty more.

He had been offered an outlet in a stupid agent of nothing and a tract of less than nothing, and was withdrawn into the desert again.

Joseph tried to find work, any kind. But he was in a country district, whose chief source of employment was the building industry which was at a stand-still, so that jobless carpenters, masons and laborers found themselves forced into the breadline by the thousand. Baggy-eyed, caustic or sullen, and made desperate by the foreclosure of homes and insurance, they jammed the home relief offices and were at the riot stage. Snarling jams of men and women burst through office rail-gates and broke down pine-board barriers in the first surges.

Full of fear for his family that depended on his inventiveness in an hour like this, Joseph, after some weeks of the vinegar-and-gall of eating the relief food, burst in upon the Mayor whom he had helped to elect with his rebel publicity. "I'm on the breadline,—all these people who had pats on the back when I was a reporter don't remember me any more—"

The Mayor was disturbed. "There are only about a thousand who have done things for me, like you, but . . . let me chew on this a while; there must be something we can dig up, for a start."

Joseph's landlord was a fine old man, white-haired and kindly of face, who kept the music and jewelry shop in the basement of the old building that housed Joseph's family. This man, in business with his two sons and a daughter, had been wiped out in a real estate venture.

Joseph owed him two months' back rent so he went down

into the shop to see him. "You haven't got it, the rent? Then I haven't got it. Did I say, 'Give me, I want the rent?' or, 'Give me my house?'" Joseph said it wasn't fair, the old man had taxes to pay.

The landlord patiently smiled. "A month I know you? I know you six or seven years. You are an honest man. When you got it, then I got it. Go set your wife's mind at rest, if you can."

Joseph went upstairs in tears. He turned everything he touched into muddy water. And an old man had called him an honest man.

They came, the village fathers, and made work for him at twenty-four dollars a week, pushing a pushbroom and scraper down the street. It rained the first day. There were people of affairs and corner loungers, on the main corner, who had hailed the reporter and winked behind the back of the writer of books. He pulled his hat brim down low over his eyeglasses, and followed his scraper's dull sound down the gutter. It was *their* turn to laugh now.

They did not laugh. Some waved in casual salute. Some simply called, "Hello." The banker with his brisk introspective manner of walking nodded as usual in passing; the two had sat in news conferences often. A prosperous man whom he had not seen at a house party for some time stopped to explain why he had skipped the last one and asked to be remembered to Joseph's wife. He glanced at the wet pushbroom and equipage. "Making the grade O.K., Joe? The house all right?" "O.K., Walt."

Joseph quietly resumed pushing the broom. He was still a

man in a community of men all trying to live through a storm.

He went home tired and wet . . . with a quick step, carrying a piece of meat. His wife burst out laughing. A woman, a close friend, temporarily stranded with them, laughed with her. "I'll be damned—; a streetcleaner! . . . ha, ha, ha!" It had looked so funny, they explained, to see him bent to the broom, wide trousers of English cut flapping in the wind, "and that lost-sheep look on your face—!"

"Shut up," growled Joseph, digging at the wet paper package, on the table, "compliments of the Mayor and the pushbroom. Look—! Steak." They had a feast.

In this hour of begging, merriment had come to break the torpor in Joseph's kitchen . . . and now quietness.

Joseph was learning to stand by and wait for the Unknown to give the next command.

Down in the streetcleaners' shed, the man putting his scraper against the wall beside Joseph's was a business man. Another was a policeman who had been the Adonis of the force. Another was a variety actor stranded there. Spitting blood behind a truck, alone and asking nothing, was a spent man, survivor of a machine-gun squad posted to hold the tide for the retreat of a routed Italian army . . . somebody's old-village neighbor come across to locate the family friend and get a job and a cure for his riddled body . . . to be stranded with the *Americani* instead. And behind Joseph, sitting smoking, adrift with his broom on a car fender, was a young man recalled from college when his father lost his house and his nerve, and disappeared.

It is true, true—the world does not know how the world

lives, till it walks around the back of the other street.

Joseph began to find his neighbors . . . on the relief line. Here was life itself, in the mist of that other torpor, the Depression. No rank was spared. But the street picked up its cross and bravely carried it.

Chapter IV

THE MAN MEN CRUCIFIED

Gradually the influence of stranded men who could carry on, whatever the upheaval that had knocked each out of his lifework, entered the mind of Joseph. Seeing how they could mark time where they stood, waiting to go on again, he felt ashamed. He had thought all life had stopped because his plan for living had fallen.

He had expected all men to point him out, and judge him. They went about their own business. Then he saw that it was he himself who had judged Joseph, found him guilty, and condemned him to the desert.

He could own no God, yet he had been capable of the effort to find God twice. Here was something.

He tried to analyze this, behind the daily pushbroom. He found two things within himself. One was that stilled life in him, that had ever moved in the glow of a world in which an image commanded him. The other was the newspaper man, looking quickly at fact, the atheist who would sit beside a man ordering fish on Friday and order for himself, "Beef."

Suddenly he saw something. One was essence of his essence, spirit of his spirit. The other was a shell. One was within, living *inside* of the other which was outside.

Now, this began to explain to him essential things about himself.

He saw that when he was subconsciously in that desert of boulders, this was because he had nothing to command him and set him to work. His mind flashed out: "The moment all of you, the mind included, is given to something, you are out of that desert *instantly*."

Now, the rest of Joseph, his senses and reactions, considering this possible truth, saw the next truth: that it was not the outer man, but the *inner* man, the essence of him, that was stunned by the things Joseph did; but that the practical part of him, the one who could report, build a ditch, move up with a gun to face what his neighbors faced, or sweep a street, was merely the hull of Joseph, the robot.

"There are two of me," he thought in wonder. "One of me goes and does, falls down and tries some other way; he is sweeping the street just now, he reported yesterday—*all under orders*."

He wondered suddenly, "*Who is the stranger* within me?" The one who had hunted everywhere on hands and knees, moaning of inability to find the something lacking; the one who had made Joseph feel wild wings breaking themselves against bars, the one who strewed all his consciousness with boulders. . . . Who was this? At times he could *feel* a presence; sometimes it seemed a voice from the far rim of the world, like a dying echo of despair; then again it was so near he could jump aside; the despair was so piercing that it seemed he must be burst asunder. He was flung on his back by the Presence whose calls had been too long unheard and who now wanted only release from the hull that would not need its pilot— The revolter within!

And down the gutter Joseph stopped behind the push-broom and pulled out his cigarette pack. Cupped in the wind his hands were steady, steady, but the cigarette jerked. His lips were quivering.

For he was all right. He had not fancied things. It was quite all right. The man within had been trying to direct, that was all—trying to get confusion back on the road, get it to drop that rotten plan for living. It was all right. And he had feared; those voices that he had heard had seemed to him insanity.

Not knowing what to call this seat of command that had been so submerged, so unheeded, he called it "conscience." It had sent him back to face a father, it had made him see his children, it had sent him running and stumbling to hide in the desert. It was telling him now in the gutter, "It's all right—old man! . . . quite all right."

Then he suddenly understood the function of the mind. The mind was the man at the wheel. Up in the pilot-house the pilot or conscience saw the sea and all things. "Reefers, starboard bow—! helm a-port—sharp!" it called down. But down at the wheel, the mind had its own interpretation. "Ah, what do they know about it!"

Joseph shuddered. The crash might have been worse. He had brooded on suicide as the way to settle it. . . . He saw that he was not a single unit, but a crew in confusion, a quarrel of seamen . . . and the pilot despairing of being heard; the mind at the wheel knew too much.

And now he could understand something of the atheist. The wheelman or mind simply had nowhere within his vista a God; when he focused his seaglass there seemed nothing resembling One through the glass. He had looked hard, tried twice to make One out, out there. And saw none.

There was nothing Joseph could do about it. He realized that he was what his mind was. If his mind could refuse to see a pilot in the conscience, that was not Joseph's fault, but a functional fault . . . which he would not admit. It was all speculation, anyhow.

But from thenceforth Joseph began to look with suspicion at the slightest thing that the mind proposed.

Which, too, was progress.

And there were times when he longed to pitch the wheelman out through the mind's plate glass.

He was idling about the house one day, after they had taken away the street-sweeping chore to give some other father a chance, when Mill came in, with a book. "Intruding?"

"Gee no,—who else cares enough to talk books with me?"

"This is a different book. It might fill up some of that emptiness." Over a smoke they discussed the book. She had a God. It was not Jehovah, no personal God. "That's why you didn't find Him; you looked for a personal God, someone flesh-like. God grows on you. God is a force, a *Good*, spelled with one O, *God*. Contact that force, and it will sweep you through all life, all things, from rim to rim. You'll be part of that force—it's not feeling, it's really there. You're indestructible with it, unbreakable."

Mill is that. Life had given her some shattering blows.

She felt every jolt; at least one of them had sent her flying backward, to thud down, hard. But she goes on. She proves bigger than the upsets of life and the shattering of her little plans. Mill is detached, vital, steady on the course. "I separate myself from each moment when things hit. We have to or smash."

"I'm getting interested."

"We can't tell. You accept just what you can accept. You can't read this book and swallow it. It's not a religion. Yet it's religion itself. Something is bigger than us and we submit to it, calmly because we know it's a current, a force, a spirit, that moves all the good of life. It's like finding and letting an endless sheet of water float you, while fire licks up right to the water's edge. Then you let the water flow through you, the spirit of it through your spirit; and you're part of it, a calmness moving for good."

"I'm interested."

"At first sight. But it isn't that easy. Read the book. But don't try to force it. Try to assimilate it and forget it. Then somewhere suddenly it'll all come clear to you, or it'll grow away. If you let it, it will show itself to you, of itself. Keep tuned to it, ready and meditative. I hope it comes through for you."

He read the book of God spelled Good, because his mind had looked up with interest at once, and because Mill is all-calm.

It moved Joseph. It felt tangible enough to be visualized. It seemed within reason. It answered questions. It suggested an explanation for gravity; here was the beneficent force holding the celestial bodies in place. Here was the force moving tides through the moon, ripening the seed in the ground, producing fire in sticks, and working the good in nature, science, medicine and mind. A beneficent force spelled Good, for lack of name, and called, impersonally, for universal name, God. It explained, perhaps, the recurrent good impulses—lost because they were not tied into the main current, the force Good. Wherefore calmness and steadiness were lost.

It suggested an answer to the disturbing question of What after the grave. The spirit of Good in the body flowed on into the force; it did not say there was another world, but it left to the mind the powerful suggestion that a *good* force must have a good plan in store for us.

And Joseph could accept it. The man at the wheel was for it at once, adjusting the course steadily, as if already that force had contacted the ship.

But suddenly the ship huddled up all over and staggered in all directions. The wheelsman had let go.

A thought—one little thought—had pulled the whole business down, in the hour of calmness:

"*Who* was the director, the creator, the author of this force spelled Good?"

Writes Joseph in one of those papers: "I must have been suddenly hit by the question: Where and who is the *fountainhead?*"

Argued the newly self-suspicious Joseph, "I wanted to know, of every river, the source; of every book, the author; of every girl tumbled into the bushes during Prohibition with gang-land bullets in her, who ordered it.

"Considering this force so acceptable, I wanted the source. Who works the flow? *Who,* not *What.* For a work so beautiful, so universal, making for so much calmness, I demanded a beautiful, universal, calm *personality;* I looked at once for an author. Can something so organized, so unspeakably beautiful and good, spring of itself? But for such a work of unremitted love I demanded a lover. A dreamer must necessarily have first dreamed it; here was the dream floating to us.

"But as all my mind so completely rejects the idea of a Santa Claus at the North Pole, a Devil under the ground, and babies mewling to be found in their cabbages; as I look at and away from a sacred cow, an anointed stick, a Manitou and a whole collection of ancient gods and goddesses, no more easily will it conceive a Father in His heaven, supernaturally above all things and never findable, but so highly contradicted by the thousand churches and temples. And feeling moved that so many follow after this or that form of the raised Supremity, when they might try to live a little more fully and more humanly and more neighborly instead, I feel moved again to protest at the temple-keepers, 'Why don't you let us live this world out?'

"I wanted that beautiful river so steadying to Mill, so needed by me, but I must have its source; shown its source, at once I should ask, 'Who created us this thing of beauty?'

"And at once it would collapse in this world of earthy earth and funerals, births, foreclosures and secret money-treaties that sell nations into another bloody mess. It would suggest a God, who, existing, must at once have turned stunned at sight of us misusing His gift, and loosed a flood again."

Well— That seems Joseph.

This is absolutely nondescript, what follows; it was the sudden vision of life as Joseph saw it, right after the fall of the god "Good":

"I was sitting in the band room of the particular concert group I play with (his hobby is the slide trombone), one rainy night, when an odd vision flashed across me.

"My thoughts must have sailed a-sea, during one of those long rests that score the trombones out of the symphony with such annoying frequency.

"Suddenly the trombone section flung slides up and was sawing away; startled out of the sea, I hurried the cup to my lips, jumping blindly into a rapid harmony from which, I knew, a solo was abruptly to come on my score; and as I quickly approached the point of start, I realized I was either bars ahead or behind, so that I must guess at the point where the rapid solo began. I guessed wrong with a horrible clash. The ensemble stopped.

"The baton man sharply rapped the stand and gave the swift glance of ice I waited for. I said, 'Sorry; my mind was away,' and we replayed the passage. But that did not wipe out the sudden undoing of the good work of all the other instruments.

"Going home, I thought of those wild few moments of chaos. I applied it to life,—all of us members of one band. The director expects every man to play his part; people out there expect music to dream or dance to, and a world is attuned and in harmony; every man in the band produces it, it is up to every man, up to *you*—for in the final analysis the band is made up of a multiple of you.

"Now picturing the band, I visualized one without a director, a brass band leading the human family down the road.

"I saw an amazing thing. The parade was a formless ever-changing confusion, going eerily along, now in squad column, now in column of platoons, now eight, now fourteen and six abreast, now a gap and now one by one and seven by nine again, followed by another huddle, gaily dancing.

"And I saw that the reason was because the band was playing that way for them—now a fanfare, now several dance tunes all mixed together, now a funeral wail, now a mixture of every imaginable thing, so that the confusion was beyond description—yet every man was playing a part well, but playing what he saw fit, according to his mind. And a mad parade, trying to attune itself to a thousand tunes at once, jumbling up behind.

"There wasn't any bandmaster!

"Listen to the crazy clash of tunes, though!—a thousand conflicting themes, running the gamut of human emotion, full of every kind of melody, harmony, accompaniment all mixed up together like a ball of radio wires,—from it lifting now an elfin peal, now a lilting sweetness, now a horrible groan of basses, a wail of weeping music, a jolt of pain, a wild roar; now sheer ecstasy, now a writhing cry lifting, as if begging release from pain—and for a moment a mellow reverberating harmony with all the band playing together, startling the mad parade. And again the jolting clash of tunes; and sudden fist-fights everywhere.

"And listening to that eerie clash from the distance, suddenly it *was* a tune,—a crazy clash of a thousand things at once, yes—but with its moments of triumph and despair and floating bits of beauty it was all at once a symposium. It lived.

"And behind the rise and fall and wail and laugh of it the horde continued the march—blundering, surging, dancing, funeral-marching, picking itself up to sweep on over the fallen, on and on and down and up again and ever on, after the disintegrating and re-forming band, after the torn hymn that made the mountains ring from rim to rim and back again with a reverberation that somehow was a march triumphal . . . alive!

"Life . . . the rumble of hordes of feet, surging on with groans and elfin laughter, picking itself up to bandage its wounds with scarves, skirts, monks' robes and a king's hat—with anything handy—to surge ever down to the dark of the hills over those who, falling, did not get up again. . . . Floating back over the bodies left scattered in gay-draped disarray on the ground, the discord died afar with a chuckle in it. Then silence of night. A wolf calling his mate to the feast. And perhaps a distant bandmaster, above, with infinitely gentle eyes of sorrow, gazing down?

"Picking myself up from the ditch with my mired trombone, I had wanted to call on some power to stop the mad parade.

"But somehow a silence came on me. Tucking the trombone under my arm I drifted along by the side of the road. And the far corner of my mind kept picturing how lovely it would be, if we *could* have a bandmaster."

Just how the rainy day in the library came back to him with the First Century episode, he cannot tell. But suddenly he fell to thinking of the books on Christianity that he had read, and the man Jesus.

He found himself dwelling on the carpenter with a plan for a new universe. He had read skimmingly through a few all morning, but he sought one book; he had no idea what book, but he sought it.

Now, when a thing lingers within Joseph, and it won't be brushed away, he lets it linger, realizing that he will know instantly what it is when he sees it. Then he takes it away with him, in the absolute assurance that this is it.

He wandered down one side of the Religion section and up the other, passing rows of bindings and colors and sizes and titles, now hesitating before one and now the other, without ever taking one down; a padfooted clerk shuffled hopelessly before or behind, scurrying through a book for Joseph in a private search of his own, as if longing to surprise his client by finding the exact book wanted. He would say, "Is this any nearer?" When a crisp-voiced lady came up to state precisely which book she wanted, the attendant escaped with her.

Midway through the noon hour a clerk with neat paper overcuffs came up with an armful and an annoyed frown. "Could it be one of these returns that came in?" she asked, and he examined the titles, from which one flew right up at him out of the bindings. "This is it," he said, and slid it out of her armful.

The title said merely, *The Man Nobody Knows*. But what it spoke up to say to Joseph was, "Here I am!"

The thing seems impossible, but Joseph had neither read nor heard of Bruce Barton's controversial book. Certain things in the day's happenings and everyday talk get into Joseph, much more passes by unnoticed. He unconsciously sorts and bars out.

He took the book to a desk, and absorbed the weary carpenter standing in the drizzle in the street, looking for lodgings with his followers.

Joseph found a building-trades worker, who so earnestly believed he had a new deal for people in his blue-prints, that he left off being a carpenter and wage-earner to try to live his dream—which at once endeared him to Joseph.

Here he saw an ideal and its dreamer behind it, in a world that ridicules, stares, guffaws and gibes at anyone who says he is not a materialist.

Again and again Joseph, following the footsteps of the man with a dream so beautiful, longed to smash one of the hooters in the face. Jesus in the pages before him grew on him, till he became, for a moment, very real.

Here is Joseph reacting again in one of the sequences he wrote:

"He (Barton) gave me a man, red-blooded, strong, and almost unbelievably tender, who believed in you and you and me, at the same time that he saw our smallnesses. I felt him laughing heartily at the jokes of the publicans, and could conceive him telling a few in return, and they would be droll ones; then facing rich and poor, I could see him silencing them all with a thud of words, these people who don't see want in rags and sores all around them. I longed to go with him, longed to see him getting the bums to try again, the weary to go a little farther, the crippled to make the supreme effort to rise—and actually do it, to their own surprise; I longed to see the vain seeing themselves, the timid daring to overthrow lions, and the proud hearing themselves talking down their noses.

"I saw him in that torch-talk in the street; I could hear every tone of his wonderful voice, now tender, now passionately moved by hate of our mud, now gentle in sympathy, and ever quietly laying stone on stone in picturing for us the kingdom he saw: a fellowship of men, built on sympathy for human weakness and a simple faith to carry men down the road to his Father's house. And most beautiful of all, I saw him beside the woman we would stone, while his living words, 'Who's spotless enough to throw the first stone?' made us huddle uneasily there, to slip away one by one till only himself was left. And near him the woman who could face the crowd with her back to the wall, but who must break down before the last thing for which she was prepared—a kind word. Even as the rest of us.

"Barton's Unknown Man swept me off my feet. I felt a longing, in that transported library, to stride rapidly back after the Stranger and touch him on the shoulder, saying when he should turn around startled, 'Friend, excuse me; do you mind letting me shake your hand? You made me see myself standing there in that mob.'

"And—I don't know. I think he'd understand."

The reaction from all that, it proved, was unfortunate.

He saw him nailed up there in the street with his chin sunk on his breast, the only rest he got, the pay he got for leaving his carpenter shop to try to tell about a world he dreamed for us, a world of forgiveness for the other man and of trying to get along a little better with him.

Such a wave of protest swept Joseph that he longed to beg the carpenter to get off the cross and walk again . . . and over it swept a realization of the earthy truth, how little we are, how little we want of such brother-love as this.

But on the other side, he saw the thousand-headed monster of creed put up by a clash of later leaders, all believed to be an improvement on the ideal that Jesus died for, and all of it setting up such a contradiction that it amazed him that anybody could think it a monument to the carpenter.

"But oh," he thought, "how beautiful his kingdom *could* be, if they'd build it."

And after the fall of Mill's picture of an impersonal oneness, he gave up inquiring.

The ideal of Jesus lay dormant within him until after the street-cleaning job was ended. Then he began to find himself regretting more and more that the universal kingdom did not find better response in the street. His thoughts were on the forgotten man who had planned one.

He was in the parlor one night, after a rain, with the beauty of the man from Palestine on him. He stood staring out through the window that looked down on the wet dark street.

As he stood reflecting on the Calvary of ingratitude, so vivid within him that it might have been climaxed on the weary cross but yesterday, the aloneness of the carpenter against the cross suddenly struck him.

And he did a strange thing.

He found himself slipping down to both knees, facing the

side window, with hands groping together at his breast, as his mother used to do for prayer. His eyes lifted to the top of the window.

"Jesus," he suddenly said, "I don't seem able to accept a God, but I'm sure you were real; teach me to see you; if you say your father is true I'll believe it; tell me, somehow; I'm trying to see with you."

There was a dead calm after the rain. But the window shade sucked through the open top of the window with a crisp sound; a light swept across the wet brick wall opposite it; utter dark returned and the shade fell limp again.

He almost shot up from his knees in the upwave of emotion that surged through him. Next moment he was standing by the street window, shaken, and taut . . . and growing swiftly composed but still unable to understand the happening, he resisted a longing to run out of that room. But he found his heart hammering wildly still—and he knew it had really been something akin to fright.

A car must have passed down the street, a puff of sudden wind had sucked the shade into the narrow court. But since the end of the rain *there had been not the slightest stir of air*, and none since the sucking out of the shade. And he would have heard a car in the dead of night. Also, what sort of street-reflection could possibly bend a beam of light *up* across a three-story-high wall, in a court-space but four feet wide and set well back from the sidewalk? Also, why that sudden stopping of breath, and sudden dread, as if some presence strange to his senses had filled the room?

The answers answered nothing. Yet a car must have somehow had its beam reflected up and bent at right angles into that narrow space, a lone puff of sucking wind must have bellied that crisp shade out; his pricking dread must have been imagination.

But a man who had become suspicious of all of his own thoughts found no answer in these explanations.

Worst of all, he absolutely could not understand that sudden kneeling, the first kneeling since childhood.

And the words— They might have been anything. Incidentally they are exactly as he spoke them. For they were so out of keeping with his character that they are printed on the mind. He loses them at times, and they recur out of a lapse, somewhere, anywhere, just as when first quickly uttered.

And, incidentally again, in the street nobody has believed a word of this occurrence, but one person.

And when Joseph in the hesitation and wonder of three years after, suggested, "I'd asked a sign, and—sometimes I wonder if that was the answer?" that person rather sharply replied, "Why must you always ask signs?—that is not faith."

Next day, a bare-headed and busy man came knocking as Joseph sat wearily bent over in a chair with head propped up in the headache of home relief and unemployment. He stated that he was the Emergency Bureau manager from across the street; if this was Mr. S. he was to start at once, as an investigator of cases applying for relief. "Can you come now? The rush is almost a riot."

BOOK THREE

CHAPTER I

THE FORGOTTEN

"All men of no account
Unknown even in their own small province"
—Didon

THIS period begins with December, 1933, when Joseph was quite abruptly picked up to go investigating home relief families, and continues into the present moment, deepening and calming, beginning to resolve itself.

Much of this interlude is really another story, Emergency Relief. There are many salvaged sections of his home relief report—but would it profit any man to know the heartaches of his fellowmen, as felt by a relief agent who was shaken by the cries he seemed to hear? Perhaps a glimpse of his reaction may reveal the change being worked in a self-centered man . . . who may thus have been prepared for the convert's path by seeing how other people suffer.

A picture or two may not harm:

"I found them huddled, shock-eyed and stilled, like flood refugees, my corner of the sixteen million families, their goods and lifework gone, and nowhere to look for comfort. Most of them are definitely wiped out, out of the race—the fountain-pen makers, the bicycle makers, the vaudeville people, the theatre and music makers, the furniture-world people, the brass-bed trade, the coal heavers, the bookkeepers, the clerks, the teamsters, the ministers and the sextons, the housekeepers and the old army of instituted harlots, the bartenders and the barmen, the barrel makers and the barkers at the fairs, the circus people and the unnumbered army that wrote articles, poems, songs, ad copy, anything—and the allied craftsmen of the world of the printed word—the legions of the work-bench and the odd-jobs laborers—all these instituted crafts and semi-crafts, both legal and extra-legal and always countenanced by the leisurely home's-the-thing world we were born in and tin-canned out of by the speeded-up processes of the machine world. This world where robot is god, whose voice is a radio screech across twenty-page sections of daily financial doings and whose revelation is the Bible in the Sunday supplements, telling us how the little robots ten trillion years from now will live, dress, spawn and lust and mechanize the planets, with the tin can for emblem. . . . Nobody will be thinking then about the little human soul smothered under all this tin, or caring a damn . . . except possibly down in the jungle, where life is life and a break in the naked skin is pain, in spite of all."

Well, and this one:

"Cries rose up in the fog everywhere, with the far sound of the gurgling glug, slap of the flood. In wisping breaks in the fog, could be seen the slow rise of the water, sucking down another house, another store, another farm—and the occupants too silenced by the shadow of impending submersion to stir out of them; you could *feel* them waiting for one more surge . . . and the final stab of finding oneself on the charity list. And I stood stunned and wanted to burst out, 'Please hang on—'

"To what?

"We were sent to go down in the fog and find these families, investigate them, help them hang on somewhere. But the best that the rest of the people could do for them was to count us off to give them a starvation-rate subsistence on the basis of the ancient human needs—food, shelter, fire. We have to shut our eyes to the real human needs—replacements of furnishings and teeth, insurance, mortgage and tax payments, carfare, clothing, school supplies, education, books, hobbies, church and a mite for old Uncle Zeke, and how about the little man's personal wants?—tobacco, cosmetics, pretty-pretties, a glass of beer, Coney Island, trombone oil, something for when the rheumatics tie knots in you, and a bit of candy for Mom and the kids, a bit of a night out for Jimmie and Joan—the hundred little things that cost a couple of cents and help make life go around a little softer, a little lighter, a little more bearable?

"Yeh, yeh, sure—right away; coming up! Honest—you ought to see them with their baggy eyes and lipstick lips and graining white skins, the women; and their baggy eyes and stilled bristled faces and cardboard in the soles over holes in the shoes, the men, going around in frayed-collar work shirts and the tiring last of hope, asking, 'Got a job, any kind, or take and clean up around good, or anything, Mister?—anything at all, just so I kind of keep busy.' Empty hands, groping for something to do—and under the dented dignity of the Sunday derby, plodding heavily down the sidewalk in the glint of sun off chrome-and-glass limousines

. . . somebody's father, nodding hello to the neighbors, and wondering how long before undernourishment pulls down Janet who had to leave off dreaming of that first-year college, to sit or stand around the house . . . and the Home relief man glancing up off his grocery ticket pad at the mother wearily asking, 'Tell me the truth—is it really getting any better, around?'

"'Uh—? Eh—. Sure, sure! Yeh-yeh, oh yeh. Sure.'

"What shall I tell them? I, fog itself, circulating around in it all day long, giving a hand to the wrong man here, the right man there, losing the way in the fog, to feed who's nearest and spread the only word around that we know: Hang on!

"'Is it really getting any better?' But who'll answer that?

"You and you and you care, possibly I. The United States. Mr. and Mrs. Citizen. We care, though we growl at the way and the performance and the attitude and the chisel. We care so deeply it hurts—in the heart as well as the imitation-leather bill-fold.

"But the counting-house Caesar who grabs the raw materials and puts puppet governments in Mexico to lease them, stirs up hates for the profits in war and makes the world a machine that throws us out of work more and more, to set up Investment for god—Caesar doesn't care; he doesn't even know there's a breadline; he calls it flood-relief and security—security for the counting-house.

"Is it really getting better?

"The families of sixteen million displaced workers, thirty-five million citizens ask, in the fog—a nation within a nation, Israel in Egypt.

"Is it get—?

"But ask Israel's bondsman—*he* should know."

Perhaps we had better jump over all that fog-and-reaction; it jangles the script.

Jimmy was able to see that at once. Jimmy was a fellow-investigator. He is a realty operator gone smash, with the spectre of jail hanging over him for a Christian intention that was construable for fraud. Also, in this lean, trim man, something bites deep in his side and threatens at a moment's notice to fold him up and finish him. He has a detached manner, a look of downbent introspection from which a lean alert intelligence will give a start and blurt, "Pardon—? I'm sorry." Sentry listening-in to that bite. The calmest man Joseph ever met, and absolutely on the level. Ever hear of Catholic Action? Jim's it.

He returned the Home Relief script which Joseph had showed him. "You want everyone to see fog. There are multiple-millions still living, a nation going on. You're close to the fog in your corner. You're the fog. And even in there, they're carrying on. . . . You live too close to the scene—it short-circuits you. Then you say, 'Look, be short-circuited with me! Life is a jolt over crossed wires.' "

"Right on the nose," grunted Joseph, and tore the script in two. . . . "Don't do that—!" the realty operator hastened to break in.

Joseph revised the manuscript and gave it to Jimmy once more.

Jimmy returned the revision at once, with an offended shrug. "This one tells us how badly a carpenter, Jesus, is needed now under the sagging roof, Relief. . . . Are you presuming, by any chance, to compare yourself with Jesus?"

"Ah, for Christ's sake," muttered Joseph, resenting a friend, who shrugged himself away with his cigarette, leaving disturbed repentance behind.

He asked the real estate operator for a cigarette, making over it a wordless truce. Jim held a match to it. Joseph exhaled the smoke, taut and short and self-condemning.

"Yours truly, again." He put the discarded script in his bag.

About that time, Joseph had one of his spasmodic attacks against religion, gods and God, superstitions and business organizations that sell myths to the public through the high-pressure salesmen: the priests, ministers, rabbis, temple-keepers and jungle-stick Rammy-Sammies,—well, such was the angle he pursued.

It broke against his particular target, the Catholic Church, "super-imposed across the credulity of man" . . . whatever he means by that in that dust-pile of papers. A sister of his wife was in the house, visiting. She was sending her children to the minister who was most highly praisable at the moment. But as her mother leaned toward the Catholic faith, and as she herself must justify her dissension, she found justice in Joseph's outburst.

"He's dead right—that's just what I've always said," she took up at once when he had stopped; "the way these Catholics, priests and all, abuse all religion is a shame—and the hypocrisy! They can't tell me; I was deep in it;—they're just what he said they are—fakes!" And at once Joseph glowered at her. "I spoke of the fake that the Church is, not the people."

Small wonder, that he had left resentment behind. Who would understand such a man? Himself a deserter, if he but knew.

Perhaps in the following paper is the clew to what he revolted against:

"Jim turned out—this intelligence so alert, so calm—to be Catholic. It was sudden. I never *pictured* him one.

" 'Somehow I don't understand that, Jim. It doesn't jibe. I can't make it fit. In a world of facts and exact science like this—and you the clearest intelligence I've met;—I can't imagine you a Catholic, somehow; a believer.'

" 'Again it's because you insist we must see through your eyes.'

"It stung. I must hold myself down. I had the answer.

" 'Intelligence frees me, it wipes mists and myths away; you draw them around you,' I gave crisply back; 'you see a God in a world of a thousand gods. But the jungle man sees a stick for God; someone else sees a sacred cow, a holy moon, a group of Venuses and Thors and win-a-war gods and goddesses. How about the Jews' Jehovah, the Buddha of the Chinese, the Indians' Manitou, the temple-god of the Shintoists, the God-with-a-thousand-shapes of the Christians, none agreeing—and all the bloody stinking wars that shackle the world and divide it into camps, Ku Klux Klans and monasteries and Masonic temples—the whole damn' clash of who God is and who's got the right form!— To hell with the human lives and the peace of the world that a carpenter is nailed to the wall for trying to patch up! . . . I thought you were a thinking man, Jim. In all this clash that keeps us from handing a united livable world down to our kids, you still see God?'

"And the calm man who saw a short-circuit man successfully offending a world and its family of peoples trying to live together in it somehow, must hold his temper down, with knuckles a dirty hue in the press of his grip on the top of a chair on which he leaned. With a smile of infinite impatience battened down, Jim replied to all this:

" 'The very clash, my dear thinker, to my small mind is but one more proof of the hunger we know, that tries to find the God it gropes for. *What*—to you—does that hunger represent?'

"I had no answer. Wordless, and those nerves all in a ball, with a hammer trip-tripping quickly on it—and, I suppose, the eyes glaring.

"And Oscar the carpenter, assistant chief and best relief-doctor our county ever had, came up with his tolerant abruptness, 'Come on, Big Boy, before you explode again—get hot, get goin', people out in the hall are lookin' for grocery tickets or to pull us apart stick for stick. . . . I thought we put down a religion on your case when we wrote you up for relief last year—'

" 'You put down Protestant, the children go there—anything but Catholic, which I'm certainly not.'

" 'Yes, I know you're not. . . . Come on, get hot, get your bag. Come on, everybody, get the hell out on the road.' "

Down "on the road," a bag-eyed woman burst into tears, upon hearing a rebel telephoning to Headquarters and smashing the rules over the telephone in order that a family whose need could not wait on technicalities might have food. "Causing busy people trouble," she blurted. "You're awful good—; I won't forget—; I'll light a candle for you—tonight I'll say a prayer—"

"Ah," burst Joseph, "save your pennies—say a prayer for the American citizens who feed the whole darn' bunch of us; *there's* your Santa Claus, your God."

And another, a stranded school-teacher, woman of peaceful mien, who had once sturdily upheld his cause in a muttering concourse when riots had seemed to be growing, asked surprisedly when her turn came at his desk, "You don't believe in God?"

"Here's your God," he wearily muttered, picking up the relief pad to write a slip for rent for her, "give it to the God-fearer who wanted to throw you out on the sidewalk."

But, he might have added, this "God" was also the ten other landlords who, without any such slip for rent, somehow forgot to dispossess the people. And the tired-faced woman who had told his attackers where thankfulness begins looked quietly at Joseph and went her way, leaving him feeling, somehow, a bit cheaper, ever so much smaller.

He told Jim suddenly another morning in a moment's relaxation, "Jim, you're always calm."

Jim smiled that little smile of forced patience again.

"*I'm* not. Good Lord, man, I'm a stuffed headache inside me, half the time."

"That's just it. There's enough cause to smash you—and you give yourself entirely to your cases, with absolute coolness and—I don't know what. Alert and calm. Always ready to meet what comes up. The exact opposite of myself. I get all tangled up with them, feeling the troubles instead of getting them out of the way."

Jim leaned over through his cigarette smoke, close by Joseph.

"The only reason why I detach myself," he said, "is that I want to save wear and tear on myself; I don't want to react and stuff myself full of people's headaches. I'm sent to do a specific job—in my small capacity I hope I do it fairly well; I know I can't do miracles, some are bound to go hungry because of me. But when I'm apart from the troubles I can see them better; I can cut straight to them and help solve the immediate moment and as much of tomorrow as I can; there my responsibility ends; I can't turn back a flood; I'm not expected to solve puzzles. I can do so much; they can do so much; if a crash must come it'll come whether we react in advance or not. I try to stand apart to fill the moment better. It has every right to expect all of me and I want to give myself unreservedly, wearing down neither my nerves nor the other person's. And we tackle the problem together."

It remained, Joseph thought, the most clearly beautiful description of calmness he had found.

Jim went on after an introspective pause:

"I was thinking—we're by emotion and nerves the same type. But you jump and I, you say, am calm. But I'm not. It's that I know where I want to go—and at once all the doubt and floundering is gone; the chance of reaction is less. . . . It's like that flood in the fog," he went on again, "that you see. With the place I want to go clearly in mind, I try to swim out to get into the current, let *its* force carry me, not my puny self. Then my only job is to clear away from debris if I can; and as long as possible keep my head above water. I know I'm in an angry flood. Yet what can I do about it? I can't turn it back. And must one man's pity stop the cries and the bones smashing about me? There's a movement let loose, bigger than I am; all my dismay and debate can't end it; if I can lend a hand to a neighbor near me, I try; if a limb overhead or a dry rock comes near, I'll try to get there and shout to others. If debris sucks me under or smashes me, that's my end. But if I can go the whole course, and reach land, my duty is do it; someone else directs that. When I try to follow that direction I make it easy for him, easy for me. It's God."

"Jim," said Joseph abruptly, "you've explained it clear as a picture. It's just," he added, "what's lacking in me. You make me understand why I react in eddies, getting everyone feeling eddies with me."

Which, it may be, is exactly why Jim was sent there to transmit this road sign to Tired's son.

Chapter II

THE GARDEN GUIDE

"Adrift, he wandered down the desert floor
And up, across and down again, alone
In a boulder waste that stretched beyond the rim
Of nothing. Drum of barrenness, it beat
With a memory of jolted sobs upon
The silence. Intellect! Released, it saw
Itself . . . and turning up again, with feet
That went at weary will where feet would go
He staggered . . . till at last, behind a stone
He left his bones to bleach beneath his hat,
And this the epitaph:
The memory
Of a sudden breath of roses anguished him;
He had to see *a garden."*

Poor Joseph. . . . Those lines of boulder emptiness must have been the answer to Jim. Jim's calmness was the sudden breath of roses. But Joseph had to see a garden. . . . He must have reconciled himself to the finality of bleaching behind a stone . . . but . . . suddenly he saw the guide of the very garden, standing there by a boulder, with hand extended.

It happened by way of, first, a violent upheaval of the

desert floor under him. His wife underwent a third operation.

Just before, he had made place in his house for a jobless motor-pit mechanic, a barroom tough whose hair won't grow where a beer bottle smashed down, but whose heart is soft. (The making of a place for Harry was a loaf which was to return a hundred loaves. God clearly sent Harry . . .)

The Luna girl was Joseph's world—no matter how betrayed. He went in agony to the biggest surgeon he could find, who set aside the king's ransom of a fee and performed a private operation for a woman who could say in pain, that if a relief knife opened her she would die. . . . And when he saw the chaos he had opened, the knife dropped out of his fingers, they say. Then they worked against time.

She should have died; the assisting house surgeon said she had somehow been *brought* through.

She failed to rouse out of ether, but only she realized that. "She's doing fine," they all said after the weary vigil.

But with marble profile up, eyes shut and never stirring, she panted, "Something—isn't going—right; something—is wrong—all wrong." Joseph outside was calmed down; in the ward the women urged him, "Don't pay any attention. *You* know—the head." . . . But she repeated—he must bend low to catch the upturned breath, "Don't—listen; they—don't know;—work—quick—quick— He stands there yet, poor—Doodie."

A ball of trembly wires waited and waited in the office hall for the house surgeon to come down and hear what she had said; none came. Then all the falling world clung to the lapels of a young interne who flitted by, begging this startled tall leanness in the white coat of mercy to hear. She could feel it going all wrong, he could feel the smallest thing she felt: she was all he had, all he ever had, that's why he could feel.

And a white-coated arm sped round his shoulders. "Old chap—! Right, old man—I'll hop right in." In a stride the White Coat knocked a tray and mop-woman staggering aside and was gone. And a nurse came where he cried against a wall. "It *has* gone all wrong; pneumonia, against that strong heart." She gave his hand a quick press; a calm whisper, "Good for you!—glad you had sense enough—" And was gone.

She came through pneumonia, too. But the torpid remnant—

In the relief hole where he had his post, he hung up the telephone. Answering, the interne had assured him that she positively could not die after the two deaths outlived. "There's no reason why she should be alive this minute," he coolly said; "that's why I'm sure."

And Joseph hung up the phone, his shakiness calming, and turned from the window in the blur that had risen, to find a woman, somebody's former secretary, the clerk who did relief's chore now, looking at him with all a woman's longing to bandage a wound. She said abruptly, "I couldn't help but hear. You help others because you say they're taking it on the chin—and with ten times the trouble of any of them, here you are, a reporter, taking it on the chin yourself." He stood uneasily there, and she added from some hesitation, "I longed to see her well, for you. Tonight when I pray I'll light a candle for it."

Again! In a worldly wise woman from town! All the annoyance aroused by credulity rushed up to snuff out the candle. But he heard himself saying instead, "I'm grateful. I'll tell her."

He had heard a stranger longing to make his Luna girl grow well. And within him a hand had hauled the atheist back by the collar. "Thank you, madam—for her."

He felt better after he had told the torpor-on-the-cot. At first she seemed not to have heard—but as he left she called from afar, "Thank her for me."

He rushed up in a breath next week. "She's up—! she got all dressed yesterday."

The woman simply said she was glad.

The incident lingered in his mind. His wife stayed up. The ex-secretary, at her relief-chore desk, was not surprised at a man who could be surprised that she prayed with a candle. She but smiled, like Teacher taking away one apple from two to show how there must be only one left. "Point of view," she said.

Inquiring, he learned from the relief chairman that she was a daily visitor to her Catholic church. He was not surprised this time. Her calm was like Jim's, a candor. He had felt futile, empty, when he had said, "And here I stand, snapping at people who say, 'God bless you,' and, 'I'll pray for you.' I slam at faith. Why, why? How can you be so steady-faced, a New York office-woman, offering a man a candle?" And she had but smiled, without being offended. "Viewpoint."

She added, wonderingly. "Am I steady?" And murmured, "The altar." Then when he looked up from somewhere at this, she said simply, "It's a little altar in my bedroom, and a crucifix. I light candles there. It helps me through." She herself tapered and wavered, like a candle flame. The flame gutted and leaned over in a breeze; then it steadied again and was a face, with eyes gazing steadily at him, a woman stranded at a village desk, out of Gotham. The face steadily gazed. He had said he was an atheist. She said quietly, "You're too honest to be one." And she answered the telephone.

A truce grew up across the bridge of talk, reaching into the boulder waste; and deadly enemies met across moments of candor, and a member of the band of the Faithful whom he had stoned brought her instant of peace to him, fearless and relaxed beside him. There were times when he felt the white robe of the band so rustlingly near that he feared contaminating the sweet candor of its peace. Then he realized that he was longing to know more about her side of it. That was what had brought the bridge, the truce.

"Why do you hate the Catholic Church?" she unexpectedly asked one day.

He was startled. But her simple candor seemed a hand from a draped white figure urging, "The truce will still go on: do not fear to tell me." He tried to search himself. "The rigmarole—they're so sure. The bells and images—this or hell. I don't know." He frowned on the problem. "*Why* do I hate it? I smashed it in my wife. I hit at it when I can, everywhere. Hell down the throat. Or a priest slapped my face. Maybe I resented the tears, after Santa Claus and the cabbage babies went out of me. And Madonna." The white figure seemed to start; he met the secretary's sharp glance.

"Madonna?"

He shrugged. "I was born Catholic," he replied. Now the truce would end. A renegade—.

"But how—?" She was quickly disturbed. "Didn't you go to Mass?"

"A few times as a child, and half a season of Sunday School." And now she wore a puzzled little frown, and wanted to know why his parents had let down. "No let-down," he growled; "no parents taught duty more."

Her calm voice came from afar. "You haven't told me why you hate it, yet."

"I don't know," he wound up. "I didn't need God."

There fell a silence from which she asked how old he was when he stopped going. "Seven or eight," he replied. She grew thoughtful; then looking up she said, "You couldn't have been to blame. You have never gone since?"

"Once. Three years ago a Green Mountain boy died. Our American Legion down here shipped him back to his old folks in Vermont; they hadn't seen him since the regiment went away. I sat sentry in the baggage car with a sailor and turned him over to them. They had Mass next morning and I had to sentinel the box there too; where it went I had to go. The bells and smoke and the priests sing-songing,—I had to keep from muttering at it, and once I laughed before I could stop. I felt cheap. That's the only reaction I remember. It seemed silly, the rigmarole."

"You just didn't understand Mass." The young woman grew pensive. "It's beautiful," she wonderingly said, more to herself than to him.

He needed time to think. Something was happening to him. He felt roses somewhere; their perfume seemed cool in a twilight garden. It came when he felt at peace. The peace she brought, a truce brought by a Catholic. It made his boulders seem all the more real in comparison. He knew he was thinking of God.

"I lay abed the other night," she told him, "in troubled thought. Something you said about your writings going so far and getting suddenly twisted, as if a hand had gotten in and done it. You said the same hand seemed to twist every good thing you did. I thought of your feeling that maybe it was God, punishing you until it hurt, to teach you need of Him. Then it drifted away and I was falling asleep. And I shut all else out for the last thing I do at night: I say the Child's Prayer,—*you* know," she urged, "'Now I lay me down to sleep, I pray the Lord my soul to keep—;' that one. And the thought came to me after the prayer, how simple, how childlike, that I should say such a prayer, to end a day.

"But then it seemed that a voice above me repeated, 'But this is the beginning—childlike—but what a beginning.'

"It kept going through and through me as if a voice really had answered and was echoing. I don't know why, but I thought at once, 'It wants me to tell him that. This is the beginning. Give it to him for a place to begin.'

"So I'm telling you."

In the desert he brooded on this. A beginning, what a beginning; now I lay me down to sleep, I pray the Lord my soul to keep. "Soul!" he muttered.

And Santa Claus, and *scatzamaurielli*.

But the breath of a garden was not imaginary. It grew

stronger. Then he would know a gust of agony and realized his longing to be filled.

"I can't find what it is, it's just a feeling," he muttered to her. "I'm empty."

By the tenderness of her woman's face, gazing so full at him, he knew she longed to satisfy him. Suddenly he felt warmed and grateful in a rush.

"Why do you fear God so?"

He was startled. But she was always putting her schoolroom finger squarely on the problem, forcing him to concentrate on it; always with simple directness she went to the heart of a thing, pointing out in him what was perhaps obvious to all but him.

Pondering, he thought suddenly of the "dare" and told her about it. And for once the truce bit its lip at the filth and the offending of a deity.

There was a flush of anger or revulsion, making very plain that the bridge was but a truce, after all.

"Why must you dare Him?"

"*I* don't know." The guide of the garden was lost, he had lost her. "Of all people to ask what happened and why I did it," he muttered, "I can tell least about it. My great mind freed me, it found there's no God."

"Then why dare a God who doesn't exist?" impatiently.

"Ah," he growled, "now you're asking."

"I *still* don't see any sense in it;—what good could you gain, how would it benefit *you*, to prove there's no God?" She was cross. "I still can't see why the dare was necessary, why you did that. Just why?"

"Because," Joseph wearily said to end it, "I must be a

fool." And now the finality and the self-weariness were such that the guide relented.

Gently she suggested, "That's why you can't face Him?" Her hand touched his elbow. Now he would contaminate her. But she said earnestly, so that he turned around again, "But He understands, He knows the circumstances under which you said it, perhaps better than you do;—and you've tried to find Him so. Do you think He would drive you away now? Must you fear to go to Him? Do you think God so narrow He can't understand what could make you do such a thing, at such an age as you were then? He forgave it—or you wouldn't be drawn searching for Him now."

"That's exactly why I wouldn't be able to face such a God; insulting Him as I did, *if* there's God."

"But all He asks is the thing you're feeling now—He *longs* to forgive the penitent," she urged, in her earnestness moving nearer to him; "just the feeling ashamed will open the door—"

"And I should dishonor such a forgiveness by accepting it?" bitterly. "Not if I have any decency left."

Now she was really vexed, biting her lip again. "Are we to dictate when forgiveness should be? You're God again."

The coldness stung. It dismayed him. His hand, half up, sank again. The futile gesture moved her hand swiftly to his elbow again.

"I know how you feel," she softly said, "and—it surely doesn't displease,—unwillingness to take advantage of mercy is just what He probably longs most of all to find."

"Ah," he uneasily said, and he felt false colors flying over him, "I was thinking just of myself; I wanted to spare myself having to suffer at being forgiven like that." He grew uncomfortable the more for her steady gaze.

"If you only knew," she said in an odd tone, "how honest that sounded,—and how that must please Him, too—."

There was a clash at once, then, in Joseph. He felt sure he was fishing for sympathy; but over it rushed such a surge of gladness at even the *thought* that a God could find anything at all that could be pleasing in him, that he felt suddenly relieved and lifted up in a burst of wonder. "Then," eagerly he heard himself ask, "there's hope? Would such a God find a way for me to break the atheism, do you think?"

The woman stood still. He was dismayed to see the brightness of tears gazing at him. Then she said gently, "Nothing when you want Him is hopeless,—you don't know how close to Him you are right now, when you can say that."

He brooded days on end over that. He had fished for praise to the extent of touching an honest woman to the quick. He could see her standing suddenly still, and those wet eyes of surprise. He was depressed. But her gladness, even quickened to tears, was real. *Here* was something. Glad to tears over a yacht, a present, a diamond? Just gladness for another. A stranger was moved that a stranger could long to believe.

Here was the first unselfish—the first wholly unselfish rush of gladness he had ever known. For here was nothing received but the joy felt for a fellowman. If this were so, and it incontrovertibly *was* so, then here, in the pure joy felt by one man for the other, was one heart at least in which was realized the *living light* of the Carpenter's kingdom—across the dust of nineteen hundred years.

Here, then, was the torch.

Joseph recognized, wholly because one human being *could* feel joy for the seeming longing for God in a stranger, that there was in the world a living thing called Christianity; whether there were a Christ, the son of God, he did not now consider. He considered only the existence, after nineteen hundred years, of a member of the human family who offered a living example of that spirit called Christian. She did not fear to raise the cross in the street, and she lighted a candle before it; she had nothing to give to himself, a stranger, but that light: forgiveness and the way home. She, moreover, seemed to practice the commandments renewed through that cross, wedding practice with belief in the words of Him Who called Himself the Way. "Who receives you receives Me Who sends you; whose sins you shall forgive are forgiven"; and she, finding in this apostleship the priest and the agent of forgiveness, made her acceptance clear in her acceptance of the altar.

From this memory of things read in that Library during the First Century search, two things stood up before Joseph's mind: the band that carried on the torch must be in some way part of the Catholic Church, where for nineteen centuries the command to receive confessions for forgiveness seemed obeyed; its numbers must be universally small if one judged by the lives of people in the street, in which the smashing of anything like a torch was notorious.

True Christians, then, were always few. He had met one.

At the end of this reasoning, Joseph knew that he wanted to consider the Catholic Church—purely on the testimony of one of that faith, who to him seemed most nearly an example of him whom the Carpenter sought in the street.

Whether he could ever come free of the atheist in him was the question. He put it aside for the moment. But could he be honest? Could he be a fair inquirer, checking himself honestly at every step? He wanted no pretty glow, no fishing for compliments, no delusions. A stranger was moved for him. He must be absolutely fair with her; no more parading. And —if he had never been before—he must now be fair with himself.

Just honest inquiry.

He thought he could try . . . with a large grain of salt, for he had jumped into crusades enough with that wooden sword . . . and he agreed within himself to let the truce continue to last.

He considered.

It was possible, supposing God to exist, that God had "brought us through." His wife's unlooked-for returns from the operating room; the churching of the children of his unbelief; the drawing of him here for this whole interlude from which he now proposed another search for God.

He considered also, that it was all speculation.

On the basis of it he could go farther.

He had a sudden thought. Would a God bringing his house through also let a blight come on everything he touched? Writings all tangled, efforts to find One silenced; even the home relief report now being prepared over and over— And the tangles he had made of the simple relief job.

"He must be both punishing the disobedience," the guide bemusedly thought, "and humiliating you to teach you. On the breadline you're learning to see suffering, instead of yourself. Maybe He lets you spoil the writings because you're all vanity in them. Then seeing you risking your job by smashing the rules to help people, He lets the door come closer and closer to you. But we don't know anything."

Pondering, he nodded. Speculation.

"The door, that's the garden I feel," he said. "You're the guide He sent from it, and Jim prepared me to know you. . . . But all this beautiful work," he objected suddenly, and shook his head. "All this trouble taken by trouble-bound people—why do I deserve all this?"

"By nothing in yourself," the ex-secretary retorted; "forget about deserving, you never will."

The dash of cold water, oddly, did not drive him within himself. He stood humbly by. She softened it. "Nobody born deserves better than death, in his own right. The marvel, the ingratitude, is that for the smallest bit of longing for Him and the smallest evidence of trying better, the door is opened . . . It's Jesus," murmured the woman. "Ourself in return for God's only son is pretty poor pay . . . but even a crumb offered against all self seems more than we can part with."

She shrugged.

He picked up the ex-secretary, who had been transferred to a post northward, at the day's end, offering her a ride home in the snow.

He found lightness in the snow, contentment in the cold, no bother in the cracks of the old car. He was unbothered by its desire to skid into impending broadsides, righting it always barely in time, with what was so obviously a random tune under his breath that even he himself was surprised when her sharp glance made him aware of it.

She said, "You're calm, do you know it? Detached."

"Oh, I have moments of that." He chuckled a whole block over it. It had suddenly sounded odd, for him to have calmness. Then it sobered him. It would not have sounded odd, had he been like sensible people, who knew what stupidity it must be to live always within oneself.

It was borrowed calm. He told her so. "It's not mine," was what he said. "I borrow it from you." At her gaze he explained, humbly, "The truce." Then she wanted to know, what truce? "The bridge into the boulders," he explained, "to the atheist."

She grew thoughtful. He drove on . . . relieved that there could be random small-talk. She did not seem surprised that he saw a bridge.

"Stop here, will you, a moment?" she said suddenly. It was the big stone pile of the Catholic church, with gathering dusk about it in the whirl of snow.

Joseph got out too. At her stare he said, "After a quarter-century it won't harm; I wanted to look in at the old church."

He pulled the iron ring of the huge oaken doors, the iron-studded doors built to resist the centurion's men. Queer, how thoughts group themselves. Let us quote from what he later wrote about his visit:

"I entered after her when I had the big doors shut; we were in the vestibule's dark; I felt at ease on a tour of inspection with a guide of beautiful selfless candor. She was dipping her hand into something dim; holy water, I remembered. She went in making the sign of the cross; I passed along tolerantly.

"We passed into the church; it was a high vault of darkness, dimly lighted by the outer dusk at the huge vari-colored windows. Uncle Priest must collect huge tolls to keep up so massive a place. But I had a tolerant mind for him too; it does take huge tolls to keep up such an effort at giving a suitable house to God; the widow's mite and the banker's dollars. We moved down the center aisle toward a far diffusion of red that touched an altar, bathed broad altar steps with wine on cream, and glowed along the rail across the considerable width of vaulted dark. Down the left of it were green sparks glowing in a frame, at the right down there were red ones giving that wine diffusion; also, overhead a great lamp shed pale blood upon the altar court. The whole effect was of peace, deep and silent and warm. And fools must stone this beauty. Then where must man find repose, away from self? . . . I almost jumped at the intrusion into my senses of a man's naked body, flung, arms out, in the dimness over the rail down there. My Carpenter. . . . This was the church of the images.

"Turning left, my companion went toward a candle-rack over which stood Christ in white-robed weariness, looking for us in the street; she slid to her knees to clasp her hands on the rail. I let my gaze wander on a tour of inspection till she should finish.

"I gazed at the marble steps in the court leading up to the altar. The creamy altar, chaste of line and flanked with candlesticks, with its center a box of either alabaster or marble covered with white lace, was sheer beauty. It was somewhat like a huge mantelpiece. It suggested homeliness. Down over it the fused glow of the candles and of the lamp overhead bathed the court pallidly with blood. It must have been part of the suggestive props—but more, it cast over my mind not blood but the unreachable steadiness of a great calm, and I understood a reaction of release, freedom from the outside, rather than a theatrical prop. I glanced up at the lamp. It was wrought metal, laced, framing a ball of red glass in which was fixed a spark that never wavered. Oil. It failed to recall a meaning to my memory, but I thought as I gazed at the absolute steadiness of that light, of the Christian band carrying the light with Mary on the first effort at conversion, after the flame of the Spirit had filled them. Possibly its steady impassive calm suggested this. I let it be. In the same instant I thought, 'In my mother's house was absolute ease and safety, my mother lives here.'" Odd, the association of thoughts.

Continuing, the paper describes the random inspection:

"My companion was still at her prayers. I began a study of the images, what could be seen of them from where I stood, in the thickening darkness. To the right of the altar court stood the lifelike Jesus, flung out on the cross, with head sunk on the breast, streaked with blood; about his middle was a towel; they'd rolled dice, I recalled, for his robes. This side of the cross stood sudden beauty, a young woman to whose bosom was clasped an armful of roses. The face, half in profile, was creamy with the sweetness of youth and the maturity of—was it dignity flushed with pain? Mother Mary! My Madonna. . . . I looked away. I had lost the only thing that had ever filled the world for me. The protective glow, the wonder-calm that only the child can know. I let my gaze wander over to the huge windows down the long wall, drop into the aisle down which we had come, and rest on my kneeling friend who by some unknowable plan had come to give this vaulted peace back to me.

"And seeing her kneeling there with profile toward me, her gaze uptilted to the altar, I stood still with wonder. The wine diffusion bathed the white of the profile; her lips were parted in a wonder that carried her whole attention to whatever she saw on the altar; she herself was not aware of her intent and wondering fixedness; it was as if she was but the medium between the light within her and whatever was on the altar, where, when I looked intently, I saw nothing. And, I thought, if suddenly a hand were to rip the flesh casing away, there would be left kneeling there the spirit living within her, that was adoring the object of her gaze on the altar. That I took to be God. I looked again at the whole altar, part for part, but had no way of getting at it, knowing nothing of its mysteries. . . . But here was a woman of the Faithful kneeling to give herself to her God.

"As if suddenly I had blundered into someone's house, turning my gaze away I stood waiting for her to finish. . . .

"And as we drew together and felt our way back up the center aisle, she said in the old sweet detachment of the truce, 'I wanted you to see it your first time when it was lighted so I could explain the different images, and the altar, and their meanings. There's a purpose in it all. It's beautiful. . . . Did you mind?' she asked under the stars, as we emerged.

"'I'm glad I came,' I said quickly. And she was glad for me."

Beneath the casual calm that seems the keynote of this salvaged record of a visit, an extraordinary change had taken place in Joseph. His whole attitude on religion had been reversed. A self-centered stoner of a myth "superimposed across the credulity of man," he was suddenly a friendly neutral asking to know more about faith, willing to let it be, longing to consider a share in it. It was as if, gone forth to hurl his stones, he had suddenly left them piled on the ground, to go into the hated castle and inspect its peace, in the company of one of its defenders who had put down the drawbridge. And he found that he could wonder in the castle, and wondering, long to be a part of its peace.

This expressed itself in a sudden inclination to enter the castle on random visits, unaccompanied, across a drawbridge left down for the enemy. He wandered in from the relief round usually during the lunch hour, when men were pausing to rest from labor, and women and children were eating lunch, so that there was nothing to break the deep vaulted silence but the muffled steps of the relief agent. He walked among the images, the plaques, the paintings and the beautiful vari-colored windows, through which the sun cast living shafts of violet, yellow, blood and rose-colored light, and he was filled with a sense of beauty, touched with the wonder of peace.

And, steeped therein, his pagan heart loved it. He began to feel at home, at times he even talked with the images, who seemed to accept the visits with all the dignity of stillness; in fact, he grew to feel them encouraging him to a warm attachment to their originals behind the paint and plaster. And he gave them names if they did not seem to have any.

First, immediately as you enter from the chapel door at the side, there was a monk, looking with disarming simplicity at you over the railing from a corner of a deep niche, as if to bid you come in. He wore a rough cassock tied with rope, and his head was shaved. He was young, with all the wonder of the mission in his eyes. Since he seemed Spanish, Joseph promptly named him Don Miguel, and was sure he had been thrown down on to the rocks by some Moorish castle chieftain, because he had climbed up to thrust his crucifix up into the chieftain's face and say, "Look—! Jesus."

Just behind him, standing with the child Jesus in his arms, was, undoubtedly, Joseph; never had he seen more humility and more gentle protectiveness than was imaged here, in this wood-carver acting as father to the Christ-child, holding the precious child as if sure he must clumsily crush or damage or drop him, and absolutely sure that not all the boiling oil in the world could make him do it. The very preciousness of the burden making him tenderly humble. He loved St. Joseph at once and spoke to him: . . . "The world is like that, Joseph, even two thousand years later. Holders of babies don't count."

Right across from him was the baby grown up and nailed to the cross, and somehow Joseph could not stand gazing at such a ghastly error, as if it were a museum specimen; a sense of intrusion sent him uneasily on down past the cross and its lifelike victim. It was this image alone, of all the images, that made him react: it seemed barbarian art thrust up at one; he wanted to say, "It's bad taste," or something to express the feeling of being indescribably disturbed. And glancing up over the nakedness at the weary face gone home, on the breast that had a hole in it, all his disturbed senses would withdraw from the picture, only to find the effect sunk all the deeper within. So he would protest at last, "Why don't they take it down?"

And he would find himself going past the cross and up to the figure standing in its shadow, at the edge of the altar court. And now something silenced by a far memory of mud would kneel with him. For this was dignity's image of Pain, crushing to her bleeding breast the armful of roses which someone had given her, in clumsy sorrow to mitigate the crucifying of her son. Joseph could feel the tremendous beauty.

He knelt without knowing why he had knelt at all, except that he wanted to acknowledge this tragedy of all time before the mother of its victim. And later standing before the Teacher in the white robe to the left of the court, he would ponder whether it really *was* God's son. . . . And before the court he would study the altar at which the jobless secretary had looked till one day he prayed across the gate at the rail where he knelt, "Whether you ever let me find you there or not, if on the last day I still can be kneeling here waiting and trying, I'll be glad enough."

He needed the quiet and the images; it all helped him to find a stillness that was never empty. And now and then some blinking group of schoolboys would burst in to range beside him, pray and run away, or some small girl would compose herself in exact posture, face lifted up to let the altar see how clean it was, how obedient the will. Then she would trundle confidently back to school. Or some adult would come fumbling at the rack to light a candle, or kneel somewhere . . . all of which too helped Joseph.

The quiet grew and grew. On the road between his relief hole and the bureau at the county seat, he found an old wooden church of unassuming homeliness, that invited visits. He loved the cozy aliveness at once. The altar was warm and immaculate with its lace and candles, and its central Tabernacle; the rugs were rosy, the images stood in pleasant daylight just dimmed enough. He was delighted beyond words to find in a side hall an exquisitely beautiful Madonna. The replica, clear and fashioned in the natural manner, might have imaged a young queen of today's court. His hunger for something beautiful moved him here to the full. . . . She must surely have been the perfect woman . . . with majesty in her simple smile. Here was Maria Regina. And he thought, "We wanted womanhood crowned. And going down to Calvary where she stood dry-eyed, sentry of the cross, we raised the peasant mother." And he came here often to stand, an outside member of her court.

Day by day, in moments like this, he was finding a garden. It was growing on him, all the more because he must stand apart . . . and feel. But is there a surer way to find one?

How much of this beauty had been due to the woman who guided him, remains unknown. Certainly her woman's understanding of his groping approach was beauty itself; never once did she find fault that he talked with images, but let him absorb and pour forth what he would; she answered random questions simply, following his mind, and drew from the well for him, giving what she had drawn—no more, no less—in draughts measured (though he never knew it) to his moment's capacity to receive.

He does not hesitate to say, in one of the dust-covered papers, "Any other way to bring me over the bridge must have killed the seeker in me on the spot; I'd have resented the smallest move to *draw* me over."

Self was strong in him still, within the random visitor.

One day she did not come at dusk to be garden guide; Joseph waited in his car and still she did not come. And on the next night he waited again, and she did not come. But always before, if on the appointed day of the ride home she had not come, at the next dusk she would come; for they must not too often be together, or people would talk, whereas occasionally offering a ride home was considered courtesy. On the second night, however, there was no coming and no message. Something was wrong and he instantly knew it.

She had always sent word before. He was alive with thoughts. A great alarm underlay them, disturbance lived everywhere and flitted about; even the images seemed wavering, the new world trembled.

Then on the third night, from out of the wavering halls came quick short steps of disturbance; and to his car came her friend, a nun. "I knew you'd wait a sign. She's ill."

The siege that had been shadowing under her eyes—

And then he knew how little we realize the strength we will draw from people who give us help, and we take the giving for granted—on and on without ever seeing the strain for them.

Then at last she came one dusk . . . a pallor so wretched behind the smile she dutifully gave him that he protested her having come to work at all—till she said she had come to work more to see him at its end and to guide him again; who else would?

For once in his life, Joseph trembled.

He had the wonderful sense to sit silent and let her droop within herself while he drove the car; now there was no guide but a slipping strength being hurried jerkily homeward over ruts frozen in snow, in a ruinous old car that rattled . . . and stopped. She looked up startled. "It's all right," he said, "I wanted to return the candle you gave." But she was still more startled.

He had stopped beside the great stone church. And he helped her out. She had left bed to go to work and to be guide again because he was left high and dry without one.

In spots he wrote what seem sudden photographs:

"The vaulted silence was as it was the first time. Darkening toward night. But now I was guide, and led her to my altar court.

"She slid down kneeling at the gate; I went to stand before Weariness Teaching.

"The candle rack was before me for the candle I must return to her for my wife. But like a man under a derby before a Chinese god with punk to light in his hand, I stood shuffling there, not knowing how to make a start at insulting the idol. I'd forgotten the instructions of the sightseeing bus.

"But on her knees at the altar gate, a stranger's pallor turned dumbly to see an atheist lighting her a prayer.

"So I took a match and a squat disc of wax and lit its wick. It spat, fought, grew a tongue that flared across night, climbed the rack and revealed a little cross over the red glass cups.

They had dead wax. The one just under the crucifix was empty. Into it I slid the candle and watched its blood-red glow shrugging up over the crucifix. And uneasiness grew and grew.

"Suddenly seeing a slot in the rack I felt for a coin to turn the stile or what; I wanted to turn around in it and get back to the sightseeing bus. But uneasiness held me there; with no more shuffling I dropped tomorrow's expense-coin in, it being the only one I had and no subway clerk here to make change; it clanked down with a horrible commotion. Now either I must make a prayer or get out.

"Uneasiness swept over me. In decency I couldn't fake a faith. But was it fake? It wasn't myself had stopped the car to have a candle offered. Then who? Sweat pricked. The pilot within seemed angry with me. I was delaying. *He* had suddenly stopped my car.

"Then I found myself kneeling with hands twisting together, crossing and uncrossing the fingers. He wanted something said to go with the candle, inside me. I tried to think of something. A twist of thoughts rose up; I twisted and untwisted the fingers again. Suddenly the palms were steady, joined like my mother's at her crucifix hour: and a stillness fell on me.

"'Mother, help me through,' I urged within. Then jumping into the maze of thoughts I fixed my eyes on the crucifix in my candle's glow with some thought like this, as well as I can remember: 'I don't belong here, I don't know whether you're there or not; but I felt you in the window-shade. But this stranger here knows you're there; she's the only real Christian I know, facing trouble to give a man a hand. She needs a hand herself now. I thought you'd want to know that.' I stopped, and thought, 'That's one hell of a prayer.' To make it end better I started the Our Father, patching it together somehow out of the dust of too many years, till it wouldn't recognize itself. I stopped.

"'I'd better get out,' I thought, and picked up my hat and got up, and went out, feeling futile under the stars. But as I escorted her across the street, I felt a little better. I had saluted, again, the God-of-the-Shade.

"I had tried the Our Father he had taught, a part of it. I felt quite a lot better and, in the car again, I started the starter that whirred around and around with the twist of thoughts till quietly she glanced up and turned on the switch for me. It was all right. I'd meant every bit of that candle."

He searched himself; he wanted to know why he did it. But no matter how he suspected self-delusion, if not bad faith, withdrawing from church-visiting to probe himself, he found the fact still there. In a Catholic church he had offered a candle. Searching why, he saw that he had commended to the God of a faithful believer her own sudden need, because she could not stand up herself and yet would help others. To a problematical God he had made a conditional prayer, which startled him because it turned into a plea instead.

He did not know how to find as judge of his own case, and dropped the case and went out to resume his round of relief calls. But if it were to rise up again before him, he knew that he would do it again.

She was up again; he had started to go home in his car and there she was, calling.

She was calm, with the look of a siege repulsed.

And she said, "I was not fighting; it seemed sweeping me over and—I seemed to want it to. And you said I have such faith. But you couldn't face Him, you thought; but there you were groping with your candle, trying to talk to Him. And —I knew I mustn't let that faith down. And getting up somehow I lit a candle from yours in me. And hung on."

Chapter III

THE CARPENTER

Among Joseph's clients there was a young woman in sudden need, who had too soon used up her month's scanty relief allowance because of some of those other human needs which are not recognized by the flood-relief budget. And Joseph did a sudden thing. If she would see him at her home, he would issue the grocery slip, overlooking some rule to permit it. She hesitated, then agreed . . . and a creeping feeling disturbed him. He had never done this before.

The feeling passed; anticipation grew strong as the hour neared. He wanted it to be the flashing eager sweep that we must bank down. He wanted it to flash and he was quickening with it, it was carrying him down the streets toward the house, it was one more block only, she would be waiting there, here was the house. But he was going past it, past the house where she would wait and wait, around the corner and across blocks till a truck sharply jamming on its brakes, stopped short of plowing through his daze. In the relief basement he stood alone again, dazed, shaken, confused, but rapidly growing conscious of a feeling of relief, with feet in receding mud.

He had proposed to buy a woman with the people's food, had gone to do it and could not.

She came next day and was pallid, covered with a shred of woman's dignity. "You're a gentleman. I waited." There was a whip in the taut undertone. In silence he made out a food ticket; it startled her out of her dignity. But he said, "Because I caused you to expect this ticket." She took it and went. Then a man came, flinging the door open. "She's fainted—! get water, somebody."

And standing wearily in church, he moved after a half hour and slid to his knees at the rail before the altar. "You pulled me through, out of a hole. You should have let me rot in it."

He got in his car and completed the day's round.

After several days' absence he came out of the side door of the church again, and saw the private-secretary coming quickly up the path.

"I saw the car from the window," she reproved. . . . "Where have you been? You haven't been coming here."

"I didn't want to track mud in."

He told her.

She made no comment. But as they went across the lawn, in the nearness of silence he felt trust and the truce once more.

At home he found the Bible where he had put it two years before at the end of the Episcopal experiment. This time he turned to the New Testament to begin to read the life of one he knew, the Carpenter. He had tried to talk across doubts. He wanted to see if he could feel out the Son of God.

But his wife, who had told him his plan had wrecked them, saw him bent at his reading. He looked up to find her half curious, half mocking, behind a start of surprise. "Getting religious?"

"Not that," he told her. "It's my effort, my one real effort to find God."

"Don't tell me it's another experiment."

"Not an experiment." She had reason to mock. From a pause he said, "It's too soon to say anything yet; but I feel I'm not going out looking for One; it's more as if He were drawing *me*, getting nearer and nearer all the time, when you quit putting up walls. I can't explain it any better. I'm trying to give whatever may be there a chance to work out."

She shrugged. "I've heard that before."

"I suppose so," said Joseph.

She had turned to resume some chore, but turning again with some doubt she asked, "Where are you looking, this time?"

"In the Catholic Church."

She looked up sharply at this. "You must be crazy."

The reading went on, a week. He read far into the night. The print was fine. He must clamp his glasses on his nose. Several times she stood pausing, as if she would suddenly climb the wall and slip an arm round him, only to pass on.

Lenten days came, and a guide offering a hand to help him over.

Lent had been just a word. Now it was purple shrouds over images and altar. On Good Friday they were to crucify Him.

And explaining the purple of sorrow's shadow, the guide spoke of penance. Penance was the stab for the nail hammered in, remorse for one's share in crucifying Him, for things done that He must remit with the Cross. Sackcloth and ashes. The sin-burdened among them would stand waiting at the door, doing penance, and would beg passing members, "Pray for me!" Some had themselves whipped, and fasted on bread and water. Today they wore hair shirts, some of them, and gave up comfortable things.

"The rest of us, not capable of that, are bound to fast through Lent. Fast means one full meal and a light collation. Children and the aged or sick are exempt, or if you work hard; on Sundays we're excused. Also, on Wednesdays it's abstinence. That means no meat, as on Friday." She mentioned another day of abstinence but Joseph continued to forget which. He had said, "What a severe religion!" She had replied, "We are Christians." This was his first glance at the life and the routine day of a Christian. He began to understand why the White Robes were few.

Going home Wednesday, the first Lenten day of abstinence, he sat at supper and looked quick dismay at the dish his wife set before him; a dish of stew. "No no!—no meat. It's Wednesday. In Lent, no meat on Wednesday."

He explained Lent and the Christian's sorrow for the crucifying.

Harry was disturbed. "I don't get this 'pennits' stuff. Listen, what are these women trying to do—loadin' you up too fast?—they ain't shovin' it in, are they, all 'at God stuff?"

"Not loading or shoving," growled Joseph; "I'm asking a lift over."

Pagan absolute, Harry's heart was disturbed. He feared he had "butted in." He tried to explain, "I didn't put it right;

you don't get me. But all 'at relief stuff, shakin' you down. And now all 'is here study and then pumpin'. Take it easy —huh, will you?"

"Leave him alone, he's trying to find God," suggested Joseph's wife.

But Joseph saw peace straining. He tried to explain that nobody was bound. "Don't get me wrong—I beg it. Go right on as before. Don't let me upset— Listen," he urged, "call it another experiment—let it fall on just me. Please eat. . . . Serve the stew, we'll forget it. I'm not bound, either. I'm no Catholic,—I'm not half good enough. But I can try to remember Christ died for fools like me."

The gravy was thick. He found himself picking meat aside out of his stew, in the silence of spoons. These church experiments,—always jolting the peace of a family. "I'll know if it's another mirage—and I'll know it when I find myself suddenly ending an experiment—when I find it's one." He was trying to fork into potato fragments, that kept submerging listlessly.

His wife said quietly, "Fry him eggs."

After supper, when Harry offered the usual cigarette pack over the coffee, Joseph reached for a cigarette, but let his hand sink back. "I think not, till after Lent."

The guide noticed him not smoking. He said he was giving up cigarettes for Lent. This she called a mistake; she said cigarettes were his one comfort and in the pressure of that relief line on his ball of wires, "A smoke's part of you. Besides, you're not bound; you're not a Catholic."

"But I wanted to give part of myself."

"But you're not asked to whip yourself."

"I want to do just that; I'd whip the past till it fell, if I could," bitterly. He repeated, "I'm giving up smoking for Lent."

Half a week later, when next they were walking together, he found himself lighting a cigarette. Seeing quick but only momentary pain in her glance, he grunted, "Here's the man who could give himself!"

A first and voluntary resolution, broken the third day. Joseph, adrift, was wondering about his capacity for sincerity.

About that time, the guide stopped uncertainly. Did Joseph want to meet the assistant to the parish priest? Here was an abrupt step among the boulders. Could he absorb a contact with the thing he had snarled at most—priestcraft? Joseph hesitated. There was a tall, lean calmness in a black cassock, wandering on the church lawn with a cigarette. "He's your age and type—no idea of church about him, and no intrusion. I wondered if you'd like to meet him." She had waved a casual hello when the man on the lawn looked up.

Joseph suddenly said, "I'd like to shake hands with him."

She presented him simply as a friend "looking around in the church a bit." In the memory of an instant's handclasp over a word or two, Joseph summed up as they resumed walking, "He's what you said. I'd like to know that chap."

She never said any more about it.

Good Friday came.

Joseph had gone back to browsing again in the cloistered peace. He had planned, when told the people would fill the church before noon when the three-hour service should start, to slip in beforehand, so that he might get a seat and acclimate himself before facing his first Christian service-going.

"When I hurried up the steps," he reported in a paper in the dust-pile, "I found a white-haired old man sitting at a table, and a man before me putting money in the basket before going in.

"I stopped there with hand half in my pocket, not a penny about me, and resentment burning. Somehow I couldn't connect my carpenter with a toll bridge.

"But the old man sadly smiled and shook his head, and very simply admonished me for thinking to turn back just because I had no coin to give. So I stood with resentment fading. It fell away the more as he said, unaware of an outsider just on the brink, 'How few have spare money these jobless times, and how terrible Jesus would feel if even one man stayed out today because of no coin for the basket.' He added, wistfully smiling, 'So few men think of even looking in, at all, only women; and it's Good Friday. . . . Look down one of the side aisles, maybe there's a seat.'

"Silently I blessed that old man. Had I gone away with that resentment, I must never have come back."

He went in to see for a while, and remained till the end. Calvary stunned him.

Among the papers of the thing he never wrote through, we found the whole scene, reaction and all.

The monk in charge was a "clear-spoken man, white of face, with a heart sewn on the black robe, and a crucifix stuck like a small-sword through the waist-cord. He seemed young or ageless, climbed the pulpit slowly for each scene that he told, with eyes that drifted over the jammed sitting of women, as if weary of searching among them for men. Out of the pause before each scene his words were shorter, jerkier, the pallor more ageless, the lean lines of the face more and more a revolter gone tired of hoping to find something he sought out there. The jerking hurtle of words began to hit like fists in the face as if to stop that vinegar-soaked sponge that had struck amid shouts and jeers across the drooping Face; and the Face with gall dripping, lifted with such loneliness and weariness to gaze at these, His brothers, that a bristled heavy man beside me in overalls hit himself on the chest, muttering with gaze down, 'Here's a punk.' "

Calvary shook Joseph.

How much of the surging rise and fall of the organ sang its roar through the senses to make Joseph *feel* the rising and falling surge of death through the man on the cross, cannot be determined. Nor can it be determined how much part the Passionist missioner's jerk of words had in it, or the shock of the cross itself—pounding "certainly on one who wanted his walls down. . . . Love, trying to embrace us all with arms nailed outstretched to wood, could quiveringly embrace all mankind as he gasped: *I thirst.*"

Those two words "quiveringly embrace" meant all the more because some hand could stretch out to answer them with a sponge of sour wine. "I wanted to smash someone in the face and didn't know what for," he reacted.

But Joseph, stunned most by that one moment of the three hours he had borne, went out of the church worrying about self-delusion.

Joseph suddenly found himself shuffling out in the jam of bodies through the doors, and heard himself saying on the step in a raw drizzling wind, "This is it; I can take a swordthrust for the Catholic Church." Speaking in a stillness, be it borne in mind, when any voice rising up must be the inner man himself.

And he stood out there on the sidewalk, hatless and ripping into himself, because he wanted to know what makes a man say such a thing. And bareheaded he stood digging into himself there, and people stared and passed by to one side.

He explained it as reaction to the crucifying of a gentle man; but he had said he could take that swordthrust not for the Cross but for a church—and till a few weeks ago he had resented that church above all others. He explained it as a word said in tiredness; but on the relief line he was never rested. He explained it as an utterance aimed to bring a rush of gladness again over the heart of a woman of that church; but why a *swordthrust?* He wanted to visualize himself picking up the fallen torch, hurling it on to the next hand, and getting thrust through for pay,—"Ah, the devil," he muttered at this; he had smashed that wooden sword long ago. A man sick of the things we do with vinegar and gall was sick most of all of himself.

It all came to this: he was doing things that were contrary to his whole nature: the candle, the woman left waiting, the talks in silence across a prayer rail; and before all this, a reporter's job quit for the breadline. And now, a swordthrust! —for the one consistent target of his resentment.

With sudden awareness of raw biting cold, he found himself bareheaded on the sidewalk. Considerably weary of it all, but not angry with himself, he put on his hat. And then it suddenly occurred to him that he had charged himself with several errors in trying to explain such a thing—but that he had not disowned the swordthrust itself.

At the same time, bareheaded in the chill of the church lawn, he saw the blackrobed missioner, his high tension slackened, walking up and down in his own tracks—working off the rebound, his own Calvary.

On a sudden impulse he crossed the lawn. As he approached, the man stopped and waited, with a calmness that calmed Joseph as he approached.

"I sat in there listening, all through it," he reported, "my first time at a thing like that. I felt every fist, and the spit; I could feel the last of life rocking Him as it rose and fell, and it stunned me. I don't understand it. I thought maybe you could help me."

He said quickly, "You felt all that?"

"It shook me. I went in for just a while. I'm one of your enemies, an atheist, or *was*. That's what I don't understand."

"And you sat it out, stayed all the way through?"

"It seemed beyond time. And this is a man who hates what you represent;—I know it sounds odd—"

"It doesn't, it's happened before." He looked casually at Joseph, who without self-consciousness told him of that dare flung up at the stars.

"I wanted you to see inside a little," he went on, "hoping you could help get me straight on a thing that just happened. I find myself looking for a God I can feel; one of your people has been explaining things. And right now, as I stepped out of that service, I found myself saying in an absolute quiet, that I could take a swordthrust for the Catholic Church. And that's the thing I've had most contempt for." Joseph paused; he found the white face steadily before him.

"I don't know why I came to bother you," he told the man, "or whether you can realize that at the moment when I said that, I was all calm—and I still mean it. What would make a man say a thing like that?" he urged.

The man answered after a pause, "I wish I knew; I feel no man can answer that. I'm sure of this," he added, "nobody of himself can turn completely around like that; you've been called, in the street. What makes it more unexplainable is that it happened to a man who offended Him with that dare, as you say you did; it comes pretty near to being the unforgivable sin; it's about as near as we can get."

"That's what left me stunned in there. It makes me understand still less, why He'd call me."

"Yes." Pondering, the man looked up to say, "There seem to me three possible answers to that: Either you've been very good, in ways you don't know; or He has some special work for you to do; or someone has been praying very hard for you. Your answer must be in there."

Without rudeness he turned and went on pacing alone. And Joseph turned and went away, adrift on these things.

He began to talk with the parish assistant, on his visits to church.

Joseph found in Father Mac a contemporary with whom to talk of random things. If he was busy he would say so at once, and Joseph would leave. An attachment grew, though they never talked of church. Books, things, relief, callings; the priest had been a purser on a night-line, some substantial family's adventurous son. . . . He found Joseph in a rear pew one day, and at the stroke of the noon churchbells the young priest excused himself "to say three Hail Marys," without explaining more than, "It's the Angelus; morning, noon, twilight; a beautiful thing. Try it." But that he never let the black cassock grow like a wall between them was the beautiful thing. Joseph grew to need the random bits he found in this man of his own age and feeling.

Suddenly the old pastor himself was strolling on the lawn, hands clasped behind him. And on the moment the purser said, "Let's meet him. . . . Don't mind if he's short or blunt; it's his way." Joseph was presented as "just looking in a bit; was an atheist, came through the Episcopal Church and some other tries."

"Hum!" said the thick-set old pastor, examining Joseph. Then ignoring him, he spoke to his assistant. "I think there's a copy of 'Rebuilding a Lost Faith' inside somewhere. If there is, give it to him."

And turning, he resumed his placid walk, hands clasped behind him . . . leaving the two men to stand looking at each other.

Flushed, the purser turned and Joseph went beside him toward the priest-house, his escort muttering, "Good thing I warned you,—but I didn't look for him to bite; must be more disturbed than usual today."

But Joseph laughed. "I enjoyed him. . . . If he had made the least move," he added, "to rope me in or fuss over me, it would have been the end of the whole business, for me."

"As to that," coolly replied the priest, "he doesn't particularly care whether you get interested or not; . . . and if you think any priest will run after you to give you light, you're crazy. That's up to the asker."

"But that's fine!" agreed Joseph, and took the book when Father Mac found it.

He met in the book the analytical mind of a rationalist who had been bred a minister, without ever taking the cloth, because of the insincerity which he said was expected of him. There passed some forty years of rationalism, and then unexpectedly Joseph followed a mind searching through nature and science, to a Supreme Cause which the searcher finally accepted, professing himself a Catholic. Stoddard.

It moved Joseph without exciting him. He thought of Chesterton. Here was another intellect reasoning its way back to the beginning, to find the church.

Stoddard sent him into "The Question Box," a great volume of answers to questions gathered at missions to non-Catholics. Here were atheists, sects, and rusty Catholics . . . and invisible stones, and honest askers.

And Joseph, with a now recognized desire to look at the Church, sat down to read in his kitchen and down at the relief office. He was ever afraid to find a question evaded, or answered without anything being answered . . . and to this day he has found the answer for each question. The book has helped him.

He had been quietly reading "The Question Box" since early Lent. Now for collateral reading he began to slip pamphlets on early martyrs and Christ's presence on earth out of church racks. He was in search of anything bearing the feel of authenticity, of earthiness. He wanted unconcealed candor, something instantaneous, that could come to him like a clear voice saying, "This is the Catholic Church; I will let you see me just as I am."

He did not care how weighty or slight each thing that he sought, be it only simply answered; he wanted not a broadcast on a thing to be sold in a package, but information on the meaning of himself in relation to Christ as the redemption promised to man.

He turned somewhere and picked up a book of childlike wonder and simplicity, the wonder and simplicity of an intelligent mind, and found presented before him a Cardinal who loved the Church and set it gently down before us, asking nothing more than that we behold "mother" as presented by a son; and Joseph could feel stones striking both, from people taught to hate.

And he found himself longing to call out, "Not that—!" By which he knew he wanted to love this mother who could have such a son as this Cardinal, stepping earnestly, like Stephen, into the stone barrage to uphold *the Faith of our Fathers.*

"My God—," he could feel toward dawn when he had finished it. "And I hacked at this."

At Madonna who would speak for sons straying.

And she and the church grew one and the name leaped across him from somewhere. And closing the book he thought, "Mother Mary."

He wanted to find the way home.

Father Mac's role, it would seem by the final result, was simply that of a messenger, come to say, "Go to Father X. He will take you up the first rocks."

But the message is never given thus simply.

Late in April, the purser ended a random talk to say, "Find Father X, up where you live; he's made for you; he's brilliant, though quite young, and so real you'll take to him. Do this."

But for his instructor Joseph wanted this ever-random friend with the never-intruding abruptness. His quick dismay touched the cassocked purser, who at once said, "Oh, I'll stand by."

The attachment would not be broken.

At that time, standing among the boulders with the convert path now definitely in his thoughts, he was looking for some token to give the guide who had led him to the foot of it. She had done a beautiful thing, when the desert had been worst.

He found the token at last. It was a simple cross, without figure, just a smooth round stem and cross-piece, all tenderly turned out of alabaster, with a gold cap for hanging to a neck chain. It was so clear, the simplicity so rare that its beauty cut him. And he arranged to pay for it in bits, and had it put in a little box for the secretary.

It was just made for a stranger who could try to guide a man on up to the Cross.

But when he stood at noon on the sidewalk to give it to her and report his decision to enter for instruction, he saw her coming with two of her family. She turned and came forward with flushed tautness to tell him it had ended.

Stunned, he stood for a moment where he was left with no ground under him, in the public gaze. Then he slowly walked away.

He stood in the church, trying to recover his senses. He alone had not seen her compromised by these meetings with a strange man.

Tears of resentment and humiliation, and dismay for a bringer of peace to a groper, stung him. Standing there before an image of Christ the Teacher, he shook with weeping.

A man formerly incapable of leaving anything beautiful alone, for once in his life had kept this beautiful. And they could see mud even in that. He leaned against the first pew with the jolt of crying.

There had been nothing, only God. Would dirty motives have met in public? She had been trying to bridge an emptiness with a truce. They'd crucify her for it. Mrs. Brown meeting Mrs. Blue would burst, "Hear the latest? So-so is meeting a man." Then putting on her hat Mrs. Blue would cluck sympathetically and run to Mrs. Green.

He was shaken by the one genuine revolt of his life. It was the one beautiful thing of which he had been capable. And with his hand in his topcoat pocket he nearly flung the cross at the altar court.

His fingers closed gropingly around the small box instead. Had he builded on a woman's sweet influence, merely?

Through the haze of tears he tried to consider this. It was probable. All his life he had reacted to the complacent face, the sweetness of womanhood. That it was not the woman but the image of womanhood did not lessen the great delusion—if that was all he had builded on.

He turned, sick and blurred and spent, to go. But he found himself totally unable to move a step. A great unwillingness held him rooted.

He was not willing to concede it was all a superstructure, built on a woman.

He knew that if he left, conceding that, all search for a higher than self had ended.

He found himself sitting in a pew with his back to the pew partition, with the church in emptiness. People had come and gone, with wooden glances at him there; he had seen them only in a corner of the blur of his mind; the rest of him was waiting for an answer to the question that had held him rooted here.

He had not dared go out of this cloistered stillness; he knew no home but this.

It was now mid-afternoon. He stood before the Teacher again, his hand still in his pocket, the fingers still around the box.

And when the surprise passed that had rushed over when he found his hand still gripping the cross, he decided, "I'll go see Father X, it's really the Cross I wanted, not the guide." Nevertheless he saw, that without the vaguely distant and ever near rustle of the white robe of the secretary, who stood guard over his groping candle, there would have been another failure. It was this that had been moving him;—call it the flimsiest wisp on which to found a faith, and be assured he would agree with you; but it had moved him.

It sums up Joseph's character. As when a child and a youth, so now. It was still Galahad; he was trying to redeem him.

Suddenly it came to him that this might be the very plan of an understanding God;—if God there was. He would know for each of us exactly the one agency to get through the wall to move the captive within: and this would be exactly the vulnerable spot, and everything would be keyed to that. And Joseph's feeling was for womanhood, and he had betrayed it, and could be broken down through it, for He had felt the thing he had done to his image and to the Luna girl. And He sent a woman to lead him, that he might restore the thing he had been trusted with.

Another blur came across his eyes. He knelt at the gate at the rail before the altar. "I can go on and look for you, now," he reported, "alone,—I'll leave her where I found her."

And now it struck him that again he had been tested, and that again he had just barely come through.

It made him wordless.

On Friday the secretary came toward him, and from the kneeling rail he saw the face of the truce. And at his agitated relief she said, with a sharp glance and much gentleness, that it was all right again, as often as their paths met here at lunch time he could find the bridge still down. "I wanted to see you through," she said. . . . And in a pew beside her, at once he gave her the alabaster cross.

A mist crossed her startled eyes, to dim them; then they were lighted through the mist.

"But this, the thought—!" she had started. And now she murmured. "It's beautiful."

Chapter IV

THE CONVERT PATH

At the priest-house in a beautiful Spanish courtyard, beside a great stone Mission pile, Joseph found Father X. He was not prepared to find a priest so young as the one who came to the door, and his stare sent a flush across the priest's face. But behind the simple dignity he caught intelligence, and a quick sensitivity—a sincerity for which there is no word. Suddenly Joseph threw his hunger for freedom to the winds. "Try to get me over domination of the mind—! It has thrown me every time before." Behind troubled pallor the dignity replied, "I'll try my best."

Joseph knew he would. A catechism course for framework was laid out; over it the priest with the boy face and the trueness of a sentry constructed what had been constructed in himself; and he included part of himself. God's is an odd kingdom. The more you give, the more you have.

Father X was much interested in the woman who could be guide till nearly crucified, and in the four books that had come from as many winds, to make a path for Joseph.

Said Father X, wondering, "With a woman like this, and those books, you've gone farther than you'll ever know. You have received Christ over and over."

At home he found a wife who said, "I'll believe it when I see it."

He was on trial before the woman who had builded on his shifting sands.

The first lesson was on "The End of Man." The first prayers that Joseph, aged thirty-four, ever learned were: "The Lord's Prayer," "The Angelic Salutation" or "Hail Mary," and "The Apostle's Creed."

God, he learned at the first sitting with the priest, several days later, assigned a spirit to accompany each child at birth through life, not because of the man, but because infused in him was the twin of this guardian; both guardian and his spirit-brother within the new-born flesh were made in the likeness of God; at death the spirit was released from the flesh and taken before the Creator by the guardian. Also, the guardian acted as messenger directed by God in the cause of his twin-in-the-man, doing what could be done to deflect him away from evil and toward God. Sometimes, to save the soul, extreme measures had to be taken: some violent accident in which the invisible guardian might have a hand, a smash-up being perhaps the only way left to save the spirit walled in flesh. Examples of this last effort were perhaps those last-minute conversations on railroad tracks, in hospital operating-rooms and in the electric chair. "But the most striking case is still the thief on the cross," said Father X.

"The more popularly understood work of the guardian," he went on, smiling, "is steering us away from danger—some narrow escape when escape seemed impossible, and in the coming of 'hunches' and 'premonitions.' But the real guard may be the 'something' that changes the direction we started out on—or keeps us on it. Much of this may be the work of the guardian angel. Very little is known except that there *is* intervention, or intercession, and that there is a spirit world, contacting God with us in the street."

Joseph thought at once of the bum who steered him home from the park, the workman who wildly knocked down the powderman as Joseph crossed the powder field, the parking of his family car off the road in the black of night, so that all the family might sleep in the car till morning, to wake up and find themselves parked without brakes, and the back wheels a hair's turn from rolling into a deep gorge. And their two children jumping gleefully in the rocking car. He recalled also the papers of filth left unaccountably on an editor's desk—to pull down a lifework and send him, self-banished to the breadline where the woman stranger stood waiting to guide a silenced man on, through Father Mac, to this.

"It jibes," swiftly reflected Joseph, "it may be pipe smoke but it all connects, it fits."

Aloud he said, "All this effort to save a man? We're few of us worth the blowing into hell."

"But the soul is different, it's at the mercy of our way of living," softly said the priest; "to the Lord the soul of the least of us is infinitely precious; He died for it."

"And the rest of us seeing a man or woman rolling in the gutter, kick another bum," muttered Joseph. "The more I see this loving God picking us up, the filthier I feel. That dare hangs round my neck like the Albatross."

"Well . . ." gently said the boy-priest, "you've already been punished pretty severely for that."

Joseph decided to keep to the middle ground of the inquirer, henceforth. He wanted a free hand for his rejecting mind, but it must sit first in review, and see all. He wanted, he found at once, a fair hearing for this spirit-world which was being unfolded before him.

The priest was speaking about the destiny planned for the spirits encased in flesh. Out of his reverie Joseph awoke in time to hear, "The afterworld He planned especially for us. We do know it must be beautiful, like nothing experienced by man, because He's there. It's an eternity, we know, but there our finite mind stops; it can't draw the veil aside. We have some hints of it in the metaphors of Jesus and sometimes the prophets,—three qualities: the joy is chiefly that of being with God, the source of goodness, joy, beauty; we sense a brilliancy, something shining very clear,—golden armor in the sun is about the nearest clear brilliancy to describe the light. And the third quality is peace, a garden. Joy, God's light and a garden. We call it heaven, paradise, many mansions,—or just God, which seems description enough of beauty.

"That's the inheritance promised.

"We speak of an inheritance, for we are the disinherited, the prodigal son mentioned by Jesus, who came to redeem us and be the door back home again. We speak of going back home, in a very real sense. God sensed the disobedience in the garden and it grieved Him, obviously; nevertheless He planned and set the process of Genesis in motion, making or evolving the world. When it was settled and ready, He waited to see how we were going to behave. So He gave us free-will, wherewith to choose freely in the light of unspoiled understanding.

"We know how Lucifer, the trusted angel, had conspired

for power and been driven from His sight with all the fallen angel's followers. Now Lucifer, or the devil, saw very clearly, for he had the greater understanding possessed by spirits. He must have realized that he was eternally done with God; then here was his chance to control a kingdom of his own. For he saw us in our first parents and corrupted them in their innocence with his suggestion to disobey God, which he made seem very sweet in the guise of special knowledge. We know how God wanted our devotion, but it must be the love freely returned by intelligence, obeying its loving father. And seeing the choice unwittingly made, a choice of disobedience and self, he banished Adam and Eve down here to live, to contend with darkened intellect: grope, work for bread, struggle, and die; but repenting because He saw it the work of Lucifer, He promised a Redeemer and a chance to earn the way back —exile's end, through the same free-will that had damned us.

"But down here, Lucifer works his system of suggestion, stirs up the desires we try to check, makes lies truth and mud beautiful, and makes it all seem life—turning us against God."

Suddenly Joseph saw this spirit-life translating itself into terms of earthiness. He saw the devil baiting the most powerful disobedience that man can know: the veil-draped form of woman, pouting across brothels, leg-shows, lustful art and the more daring revues; he saw a pseudo-intelligence bringing back pagan Rome on a modern plan on which no Rome could have lasted a century—in a suddenly connecting movement expressed in sterilization, selectivity, birth control; plowing-under of religion, morons and moral restraints; corruption of education to liberate flesh: free-love, nudism, wage enslavement of the crowd for the benefit of a highly organized (and powdered) patricianship, with at first a diluted and impersonal First Cause for God, which would painlessly die out of mind and leave the intelligent man free . . . free to be himself, Antichrist . . . the very thing Joseph had espoused.

And he saw life trying to make a living—a family squirming over all the face of the earth, always in pain and always covering it over with an effort to find a sop; he saw the human parade of lust, greed, pride, hate, bigotry, intolerance, setting up those bleeding walls of flag, sect, race, and party—and forgiveness striving against ingratitude and losing the fight—neighborliness being slowly beaten down by converging surges of gossip, jealousy, suspicion, smallness, anger, sneakiness and treason, and charity going to its stewards, and law going to its buyer,—all the limping ghastly effort at justice-to-man going to rack and ruin by default of reinforcements in the moment of discouragement, in a world that smashes the just and puts up statues to fat-bellied blights who can bray like asses. "My God," Joseph, who wanted beauty, burst out, "what a field for a kicked-out Lucifer to go whispering about in, sowing dragons' teeth—."

He felt suddenly a feeling of fellowship with the man-in-the-street, the composite being he had so callowly quoted in his news dispatches to the city. He softly said, "We haven't the ghost of a chance."

The priest came back from the hall, where he had been arranging appointments for some young Protestant woman and two men who came, one after another; they seemed to prefer this one of the three priests for their try at conversion. "What are we trying to reach, I wonder?" Joseph thought, his mind lingering on their voices as Father X sat down with his shy apology: "We'll try again, before the doorbell rings again." And took the blotter-block off his catechism, to resume.

"*Why*," Joseph asked, "must a God so understanding have us hand down a world like this?—we haven't mended since the flood—we're worse."

"The same free-will," replied the priest, with a bit of sadness in his smile.

Then resuming, he put what he had down simply on the table.

"You must try to visualize a Creator, whose *majesty*, whose simple dignity wouldn't know how to accept a human state *compelled* to be good,—who certainly couldn't accept an obedience *forced* from his creatures. Remember, this Loving-kindness is the same God who could give an only Son to assume the indignity of our human nature and let Him be crucified like a common thief, so as to make that nailed-up flesh stand guilty for man's disobedience for all time, because He wanted His exiles forgiven. Remember too, that all He asked as a condition to our being accepted fully back in the garden He had made for us, was that we acknowledge both the offense and the offended Creator, and *ask* to be lifted back home, with what small love we're capable of. Just that little was enough, and He lifted the thief down off the cross with pity and tenderness."

"Good Lord—," burst Joseph. He sank back broodingly into the small silence which he found the priest meditatively sharing. Their glances met. The young face smiled.

Said Joseph, "I see. To have such a God coax or force our

admission of smallness, to get us back home, would add—"

"Insult to injury. . . . Then, free-will is the direct gift God gives, to man alone, by which to choose redemption or the short life of the earth. He's fairness itself. We don't have to be good. We can make our exile very pleasant, with flesh or with grain gotten at someone else's expense; and by putting aside anything unpleasant we can make a very acceptable heaven of it here—and in fact, we seem to," he said with that sad bit of a wondering smile. "So often, choosing not to see beyond the grave—taking our chances on whether there's eternity to answer to, afterwards. Or we can choose to deny ourselves—or just try to—the effort counts; this is the only place in all life," he said, "where the *intention* is counted and the performance discounted—or even ignored altogether, when one has *tried* to break through himself, for God."

The sheer beauty of it—

The priest went on, "He gave this free-will not to a dark dumbness but to the highest handiwork of His Genesis, to man who had already received the light of understanding. With the extra grace, He looks for remorse,—love, from a man forgiven the unforgivable."

"And this clearness we use," murmured Joseph, "to choose our destruction."

Against this human trend, the priest went on to say, God employed guardian angels to try to deflect us, as well as prophets and holy men to teach and warn us, seeking the co-operation of truth implanted in the conscience. Finally Redemption was sent in Jesus, who set up his kingdom of charity in the heart.

And now from this and from books, Joseph understood the Redeemer, His work done, leaving with us His abiding spirit under the sheltering roof of the Mother, that she might burn the vigil lamp. Until from the night should come the prodigal son and daughter; and refreshed with her tears and bread, they would hear how to ask the Father for forgiveness while she cleaned their coats before sending them on, kissed and silenced with tear-streaked cheeks, hand-in-hand up the last path to seek the Father with a mother's blessing. . . . After God only knows what concourse of saints and patrons, the friends-at-court, had interceded, that two more might be sent on like this, when worldly life wanted the heart to dance instead. Mother-at-the-lamp, waiting for the dance to end . . . praying . . . waiting under the cross in the long night.

And thus he understood, at last, the mission of the thing he had hated, the Catholic Church . . . of whom the late Cardinal could so simply say, "To know her is to love her."

The priest took up the subject of prayer . . . and here a wry taste died out of Joseph's senses.

Prayer, he learned, was not an inane ritual of "holys", but a beginning, the first beginning, a man trying to lift all self to God. Here Joseph uneasily told the priest he had made a stupid if not offending thing of it. Asked how, he said: "Just talking from the moment, taking a chance on talking to emptiness or a God, but trying to feel One, sometimes to thank Him, sometimes to say I understand a little better and will try to go on from there, sometimes I simply ask a lift over a tough spot—"

"But that's prayer," softly said the priest.

The priest took up the Lord's Prayer. "It remains the one perfect prayer we have. It includes all in so little. Only God Himself could have constructed it." One of us in the street had asked what to say in a prayer, and the Carpenter had told him.

"It takes in all that a prayer should have," the priest went on. "In fact, it's a group of separate petitions, seven of them. Let's break it down:

"The first four acknowledge God our Maker and the others put us before Him personally asking Him to sustain us.

" 'Our Father, who art in heaven; hallowed be Thy name.' Notice how Jesus first of all acknowledges the universal Father, and places Him above all life. Then in a second petition, with intelligent humility He has us salute the name of Divinity. There, is love, the created, honoring the benefactor, the Creator.

" 'Thy kingdom come.' In three words he has us all remember that we are sons and daughters of Adam and Eve. In a family a member stands by all the brothers; the pain of one is the pain of all—that is," and here he smiled, "it is supposed to be, which it seldom is. Even in our house we forget our own brother; then how can we run to help a total stranger, maybe of another color? Yet through Adam—and by Jesus who made us brothers in His death and gave us His mother for our mother—we're all twice brothers. 'Thy Kingdom come.' Here we long to see the brotherhood of man grow—we long to extend love, help the next man get back home with us to our house in heaven; and to help someone in the street or in the swamp. With the mother we try it, this is the house of Christ, we all try to return home together. Out on the road you try to help whenever someone slips. Prayer is still a quick way to help make 'Thy kingdom come,' when our material help fails."

"I see."

"'Thy will be done.' Here is the whole world of obedience. Whatever tries to break you down, you bear, if by bearing it you're standing by the teachings of God. But you're trying to carry on and suddenly temptations come. To give way is to take advantage, push somebody, make your hold stronger, or get out of doing something troublesome but right. But you will to honor God, stand by the good and the right, do your duty. 'Thy will be done.' Surrender of self to the Father—sink or swim. Here trust and obedience are complete. His will is your will. Four words that mean eternity to you—words that please Him.

"The rest of that petition is important. You want His will to prevail, 'on earth as it is in heaven.' That is, you pray for obedience down here like that of the angels and souls in heaven, where, of course, submission of the will to the Will is perfect. You ask persistence to hold you to that model. We'll fail badly, because flesh wants us to go the other way; but He understands and helps us accordingly.

"Now we come to petitions to help us get through exile. We call that asking for temporal help—the opposite of eternal. Or material, perhaps, contrasted to spiritual. We need both kinds.

"'Give us this day our daily bread.' Sustain us, help us find jobs, help us hold our shop or ship or factory or farm, help us to get through. Don't underestimate this petition;

He is glad that we can ask for bread today, as well as for salvation tomorrow. It's not a strain on God's dignity to ask for coal when you're worried because your children are cold. Giving an answer to a man praying for coal, by moving someone to send him some, might save a desperate father's soul; he might have done something rash under pressure or he might have lost faith. And to God, if to no one else, a soul is infinitely precious: He gave His only begotten son."

"What a rebuke to us in that," thought Joseph; "we let them smash and bury them on the dump."

"Well, life. . . . The next petition gives a jolt to most of us. 'Forgive us our trespasses as we forgive those who trespass against us.' Analyze that: forgive us *only insofar as* we forgive the man who hits us. You're asking God to forgive you to the extent that you forgive the next man;—so that if you don't forgive, you are petitioning God *not* to forgive *you.*"

"Oh–oh— Then few of us are going to be forgiven—that petition boomerangs back on us—"

The priest cautioned, "Well, it's pretty hard to expect a man to forgive a man who wrecks him, for instance. We have to remember the life we live in; it's—not encouraging to forgiveness."

There settled a pause. "You seem to have a very human viewpoint here—if an inquirer may say it."

"It's Christ. . . . That petition does give us trouble," admitted the priest. "We don't feel very glad to know that the most-said prayer is also the one most abused—unintentionally. If people would only analyze it . . . 'forgive me *as* I forgive others.' We sentence ourselves, every time we petition that and don't forgive. We don't know what we say."

He went on:

"The concluding petition is obvious, 'Lead us not into temptation, but deliver us from evil.' You recognize the power of God, Who can command all eternity, to pull you out of holes, and strengthen your will against temptations. The Amen at the end means 'so be it;' sort of God's seal on the petitions."

Joseph began to feel the structure of life changing.

There was an interior realignment going on, of which he was aware, as if Genesis was struggling to come out of the clutter of the past, within veils. Here his mind helped him. His intelligence directed all the process of unveiling the cornerstone. He was not surprised. It had been honestly laid, that foundation. The same mind stood ready now to consider the construction worked out under the supervision of the priest.

"If we're wrong," he mused, speaking to his wife, "twenty centuries made the mistake. But I'd like to go to the grave with it. It answers: who am I? where to? where from? and much of: why do I do what I do? And I'm damned if I ever had as much as one question answered, anywhere else."

She said nothing. By this Joseph remembered that he was on trial.

He was grateful to the Catholic Church, at the outset, for that. He wanted to be on trial; he had enough to take the docket for. Now he could try himself. He understood his tangle of motives, desires, suppressed wants, and furtive thoughts, a little better,—much better. Now he could try himself through a reasonable point-of-review: free-will. It made him absolute monarch of his destiny—whether there was a heaven or no. No matter how he checked, still it stood. By it man chose poverty or bribe, advantage or let-the-other-fellow-live, a good time about town or reins on self. He could choose sanity or destruction. God or the moment.

But beast or beauty. It put it right up to the man.

And the guardian, the twin spirit. Here was material for a world to build, such as his little mind had never dreamed of. For once, its beauty was clear, it shone of God. It gave him a Being seeing to the gravitation of the stars and the lifting of some poor devil fighting pressures alone somewhere, overwhelmed among temptations. A God like that . . . and this twin-spirit brother ever running up hacking and thrusting to get to his side, after shouting out warnings enough, never heard—he wished he could let him know he would try to hear better, from now on.

He named him Joe. He had to identify the guardian somehow.

The lessons went steadily on . . . to the stumbling-block of childhood, one God in three parts. The Holy Trinity.

"In God there are three Divine Persons, really distinct, and equal in all things—the Father, the Son, and the Holy Ghost."

Here the teaching was simple, and the Word drew the veil over God, and left it there.

He who accepted Christ the Teacher, accepted God the Father, sending the Son for redemption of the many, and accepted the Paraclete issuing from Father and Son. The trembling fishermen and the publican and the others, eleven strong, hid from their seething nation in a house with the mother of the risen Son, till the promised Paraclete descended in the form of tongues of fire and filled these huddling Jews, transforming them, so that with the mother, issuing forth into the street of violent danger, they scattered and spoke in the streets with a fire that converted three thousand. And the Church began that same day.

Now, here was material enough either to shatter or to put substance into Joseph's mist-raised cornerstone.

Here was either God in action fulfilling Genesis, or here was the end of inquiry. And the youthful priest knew it.

He laid what he had on the table, and let it stand, a crisis on the third step of the convert path.

"There is God, supreme and infinite, one God over all the universe, with no equal; God can't have an equal. By the very nature of God, there can be but one God, one First Cause, one Creator.

"We call that, the *nature* of God. A state of being, the force that shaped the world and directs it. The Oneness, God, *Godhead.*

"But this nature is shared by *three distinct persons,* who are co-equal. It's hard to grasp. It's the cause of a lot of trouble. Yet if there was any reason for Jesus to have revealed more than He did, and for the Father to have revealed more than He did, and the prophets, some reason necessary for an understanding of God beyond what He chose to reveal, it can be surely believed that it would have been done.

"All God has chosen to reveal of Himself, is that God has *one nature,* shared equally by *three persons.* If you can think of three men somehow seated together as one mayor, we'd have three distinct persons with equal power; each is mayor, all share the nature of being mayor, but they are three—"

"I understand," eagerly said Joseph.

"It's a very imperfect example—"

"I know," quickly, "but it helps me see a Godhood shared by three equals, one God in three who are persons."

"Yet how and why that can be—"

"I'm not asking, they didn't say—"

The priest smiled as he checked this. "Don't think of God as They. . . . God draws the veil on all else but what you just now understood." He asked, "Can you accept this for God? Is it enough, what is revealed of God the Trinity?"

After a moment, "Yes. I don't ask more."

"Why?"

"I don't know . . . if that's all He saw needed to be told us, I want my questions to end there; I know He assumes no reasonable man who wants to believe His word will ask more than He tells." He pondered. "I assume a God who could die to crucify all our disobedience on that cross and could open the door back home for us again, is a God who also understands our intelligence; intelligence could put its trust in that God no matter how He draws the veil; that's the kind of God I'm trying to find, anyhow, and if I trust Him I trust His silences too."

"It's—great," softly answered the priest, with such simple gladness that Joseph felt embarrassed, "to hear just what we hope for, like that. That was what I was afraid would give trouble—it generally does," he said, smiling.

He went on, "He doesn't want blind or unreasoning faith; but He does want trust, in proportion to the capacity for reasoning. He wants us to think, and more is expected of more intelligence. And the more the intelligence, the greater the trust; some of the simplest faiths are those of the greatest minds, that can accept silences and use their own minds on deeper revelations, finding reasons for their faith. Then there are some of His children who, for His own reasons," and here again he gently smiled, for these seemed points of much debate, "He has darkened, so that they're simple-minded, or even half-wits, or have to be taken care of altogether. The same God accepts the childlike faith and the incapacity for faith, in the simple, the half-wit and the idiot."

Joseph, his mind going along with these things, felt the foundation solidifying, and calmness beginning—his own calmness at last. He nodded. "If a mind covered over just takes all on faith, or sees a twisted picture, or sees just a blur, allowance is made. . . . Suppose later my own mind challenges the acceptance I have just found?"

"Then let it, keep all walls down. . . . All we can do is pray the same God once accepted, to help us over the hole again."

Life steadied into clearer lines, simpler focus. He was getting his bearings.

The lesson on sin opened another place through which he could consider himself. Looking through the new breach, he thought he could now see the why of chaos, in a man who had been stunned by what he did. He had given his reins over to gods he never saw. Yet surely he had set them on seven pedestals, about the great god Self.

These seven were now identified by the priest. Pride, Covetousness, Lust, Anger, Gluttony, Envy, and Sloth. "The chief sources of sin . . . are commonly called capital sins."

He recognized them all. A babbling madman, tearing into shreds an oilcloth book, had swept them all off the shelf and gone, stilled and emptied, into the desert.

Now he began to ponder over them. There were two kinds of sin in the eyes of God: original sin, or the disobedience of the first parents, visiting labor, worldliness, corrupting temptations and death on man, in the instant of birth; and, actual sin, which we ourselves commit.

This actual or world's-life sin was further broken down by the priest into two kinds: mortal, by whose grievous nature man stood cut off from God till absolved; and, venial, a lesser offense, or a grievous one committed without full consent of the will.

A mortal sin cut a man off from God, destroyed his inheritance and sentenced him to hell, this hell being understood to be primarily an eternal anguish, the separation from God Whom the soul too late has come to understand and must forever lose.

"God knows how utter the punishment for mortal sin," Father X told him, "so He made it very hard for the normal man to fall into such sin as that. In fact, for a reasonable man it's almost impossible. In order for it to be a mortal sin, the act has to be deliberate; it must have the full consent of the man; he must know with absolute certainty that he is proposing to cut himself off from God for all eternity. And he must be in full possession of his faculties at the time. The free-will must act completely, he must wholly want to do what he does.

"If there's unwillingness; if you don't *want* it to be and it overcomes you; if temptation swept you away—and especially if you prayed to be delivered and it swept over you anyway—or if you know nothing about God, through native ignorance— You see how hard it is for a just man to be in mortal sin.

"But deliberately putting yourself into the *occasion* of sin, condemns you if you give way. For instance: a lustful man who's been forgiven for falling under the influence of lust, and who continues to *expose* himself to it—by seeing dirty shows, or pictures, or books, or going where the form of woman will be before him—what can he expect but temptation will overcome him? Could you see less than the eternal death-to-God, in case he should get killed after the act and before he had a second chance to plead forgiveness?"

And Joseph going home took down a beautiful little undraped painting, the last of the old Life-plan . . . because he must ever fight the sway of the god Lust. "Joe, Joe," he called on his twin, "show me how to take the picture out of me—"

Down in his territory was another woman on relief, one whose personal refinement he could respect.

He was on the couch where he usually drew up the regular relief order . . . and was startled to find her arm round him, her body drawn to his, her lips close to his face. "Let me,—

for some time I felt—" He sat taut, here was a thing that had never happened to him, and a fire he had thought banked leaped over walls—.

But in that flare two strange barriers rose up.

His effort to rebuild on God had been made without a conscious submission to God in his inner life, thus awakening a great doubt within himself about his capability. Suddenly in the flare-up of this woman he felt the half-built new structure within him facing red ruin. And for the sake of that framework he suddenly wanted his fire controlled—and an unknown wall rushed up, behind which *he sat absolutely cold.*

He felt at once the impossibility of this, but there was no time for debate: groping about him, a woman was being swiftly carried away by emotion.

He had just time enough to plead, "Lord, be kind to this honest woman—" and then he sat relaxed, calm.

Without breaking her hold for fear of precipitating a reaction, he cast about for something to help her and said as gently as he could, "Look, don't let it get away from you but don't try to choke it back suddenly; it'll upset you;—and whatever you do, remember that I understand, I've gone overboard myself and nobody around respected me enough to pull me clear."

She hesitated with her arm around him. She protested: "I thought you'd—; you would be different,—not cold, I thought."

"I'm anything but cold—it's a fight *not* to let it carry me; your first thought was true." He spoke more calmly.

She vaguely stroked his back, her arm sank down and she sat by, the fire flowing out of her face, and doubt creeping over the ebb with a vague—relief that it had not happened? —who'll know? The next reaction would be a woman's self-respect seeking a rag of dignity, and he cast blindly about for something to stop the stab of it.

He plunged, still calmly, "I'm as surprised at myself as you are; suddenly I just couldn't let us suffer the reaction that would come after." She looked up quickly at this, and sensing the right track he went on, more earnestly, "As it is, next time we meet we can look each other in the face; we're human beings, pulled this way and that by things rushing up from nowhere; my mother could understand that, the same as you will tomorrow."

"You won't despise me—?"

He put his arm round her shoulders, and released it; he was honestly moved to do this. It eased the rebound for them both. Her face wore a dazed look; he smiled, "It's buried. We'll leave it right here. The whole thing belongs to the moment and we mustn't think of it; we didn't let it burn us; it jumped across us and is gone where all the minutes go. . . . What was that store you buy from—?" He resumed scrawling.

Two blocks away he drew the car to the curb and wiped his forehead. Trembling at the wheel, he had had to stop the car. He thought: "It isn't possible—but, God, if it was a test again I don't know who stopped me this time; I didn't stop myself."

He forgot to think of "Joe" till long after. But he included the incident in his report to both the guide and the priest, wanting them to decide whether this was Intervention.

"It's sincerity," said the priest, "the thing you suspect yourself not capable of."

Muttered Joseph, "You wouldn't be too sure it's that, if you knew all my little dodges and heroisms."

Next day on a pretext he called back, to be sure the young housewife could see that he wasn't remembering. And she told him, "Honest, you're a square shooter" . . . and he drove away very embarrassed.

He could fish for compliments. But a good word unsolicited threw him into confusion.

"Just like my father," he shrugged. And there the incident rests.

There was a violent upheaval, shaking the whole structure, just as it was beginning to be practical earthiness, and daily Christianity.

Going to Jim the Catholic, he thanked him "for that direction you gave me in the flood." And told him he was feeling his way through the Catholic Church.

But Jim looked sharply at him. Then calmly he called him deluded—"Roped into the good old business house, the Catholic Church. I thought your intellect was able to see through the farce."

"What do you mean?" asked Joseph, in the shock.

"Why, my dear man—it's unquestionably what you said. I took the opposite side of the debate, for the mental stimulation."

"So you're not Catholic. That it?" tautly.

"I am; I can't help that, we're born this or that. But the farce;—it's unquestionably a business proposition, run by super-salesmen; the most brilliant minds are found in that racket. *There's* your proof of whether it pays. . . . I've got to keep the pretense up, for my small family's face."

Joseph was sunk by this.

He drifted on down the highway to his part of the relief line, aware too of a smouldering fire . . . which proved to be, in Father Mac's office, not the new structure burning down, but an affection hurt. He had warmly liked Jim.

The ex-purser was quite angry.

"There's one of our Catholics for you— So, we're money changers—; I'd love to meet that chap—; I'd make him show every argument he has—and I wouldn't have to let this 'business proposition' so much as answer," he said, aroused; "we wouldn't need to—; nothing to answer."

"I don't know why, but I can't find myself angry with Jim," Joseph broodingly said. "I'm partly here because of his calmness; he's the clearest intelligence I had met."

"No intelligent man could do this thing—that's absolute lack of reasoning; it isn't even an argument."

"Father, he's an intelligent man. I've felt that out," wearily said Joseph.

"That's friendship," curtly said the priest. "And his way of earning it is poor gratitude. He might have smashed the faith in you;—I'd love to talk to this Catholic."

The incident was sealed, leaving no breach between the two in the relief agents' room; but the nearness had gone. Joseph felt that one whose light he had trusted, had suddenly put water in the lamp. And reefs everywhere.

This made him search the thing put before him in the

priest-house more cautiously in search of delusions . . . he was fearful he might find one.

One dusk, when he arrived too early, he found Father X reviewing a woman convert.

Joseph sat with a Scot and another man waiting to report, in the outer office. A drizzle grayed the garden about the Spanish court. He murmured something about "this veiled world" . . . and about men "wondering what to want, and then finding yourself looking in the least expected place, without knowing whether to want it."

But the Scot said sharply, "If ye feel that way, I do na' know wha' ye're here for."

"If I knew all the answers, I wouldn't have to go trying to find who's got them," Joseph replied over an effort to bank smouldering fires. "I hope you know why you're coming here, clearer than I do."

"I have a motive," the answer came stiffly.

The priest quickly felt the smouldering, when he opened the lesson, and Joseph told him. "I didn't know you needed a motive, to consider a God," Joseph said. "If I told you I knew what my mind was going to accept tomorrow, I expect you wouldn't waste my time here, for you'd have nothing to give me. I don't know why I'm taking this course, I don't even know if I want it or only long to want it; I know only that I'm here—and glad to be here."

Spasmodic moments like these jolt the entire stretch of the convert path . . . and are best left unreported. They were jolts recorded, perhaps, in the skeleton frame that was rising on the foundation of—of what? Longing for faith? He never knew whether it was faith itself. . . . But, more probably they were but jolts upon the fibres of Joseph rather than upon the framework of the New Thing. Jim had hurt, shaken.

But the hammer-hammer disturbance of raising a new world in the mist went on. . . .

In a desultory paper in the dust-heap, he calls them "re-birth pains."

In the self-mockery of which Joseph is revealed once more.

Father X was not the only priest on the garden-court knoll to deal with this burden. All three had turns, when the boy-faced earnestness was away on a call, or had too many convert hours (they sought him so).

Suddenly it was the pastor who came, a brusque, dusty-lean, hard-bitten, but just man, with the care of one of the largest and most trying suburban parishes. This parish runs the whole gamut of life. That will give some idea of the pastor.

Joseph, finding this leanness coming in with rusty cassock and dented skullcap one night in place of Father X, sensed at once a need for insulation. There was the formality of a nod and an immediate sitting down to the catechism.

"Heard quite a bit about you; Father X is out somewhere; Lesson Nine is it—Effects of the Redemption?"

"Yes, sir."

"See you're making strong strides."

"I think we're finding the atheism willing to let a thing show itself—"

"You're not an atheist," snapped the pastor, "drop it."

"I'm not tickled to death to be," he said wearily, and drew a look.

"All right," calmly enough. "We'll take up the two kinds of grace: sanctifying, which is the grace that makes the soul holy and pleasing to God; with it you are an adopted son of God, it's what the soul loses when you fall into mortal sin; it's the grace that makes saints, so you can see how rare co-operation with it really is all through life; yet God gives it to all to help us try to live just lives, through Him. And, actual grace is special help to get us over holes, give us light, strengthen us to bear up when pressure wants us cracked down, and brings us through by strengthening the will to resist temptations; the kind of grace that turns us in the street, for instance, looking for God—without grace it's impossible, we can't turn ourselves—"

"I see. I wonder—" mused Joseph.

"What—?" distracted from the lesson.

"It helps explain how it happened—and me here now—after that dare flung up—"

"What dare?" at once.

Unwillingness brought the pain of it up once more.

"It's a wonder," grunted the pastor, "He didn't pitch you on your nose; you can't possibly realize the smell of it."

"It grows and grows," wearily said Joseph.

"Well, I suppose it does, too, when you'd forgotten. 'Strike me down!' you call. He's going to drop everything and serve you? Not that you didn't deserve it right then. But isn't it Divine dignity to let you go off cocky and build yourself up, down through the years, the affair forgotten, and you up high within yourself? And then—Smash! Down comes your delayed answer, and the ruin growing and growing wherever you wander," with not unkind dryness.

Different priests. And some gently wondering, and others crisp, with a mocking bite—and all presenting the one thing. More and more Joseph felt his own act tied round his neck . . . and was glad of it.

The pastor was the first to introduce the existence of a thing altogether absent from Joseph's consciousness. Hope.

Hope's mother was Grace. Her sisters were Faith and Charity. Joseph remembered the portrait of the Three.

The pastor explained the advent of these in the consciousness, growing from Divine grace.

"We have a description for Faith. It's the Divine virtue by which we firmly believe the truths which God has revealed."

"I see. Then what I've come to," reviewed the myth attacker, "is putting the cart before the horse. I find that I've believed the world of God, just as it came before me, ever since that candle and a stranger who troubled to bring it—without knowing whether in the end I've accepted God or not."

"Then," for once at a loss, "how can you accept His word? And how do you know it's God's word?"

"Because of the beauty; and answers for questions. It completes." This he must now explain, without hope for it. "Humans can't give us completeness; we get a scattered fact . . . and another piece of the truth proves it a lie. Faith gives me a whole truth and it's all suddenly beautiful. . . . I didn't explain anything."

"You did. You'll end up standing by what you think true; and that's all that's expected. Sorry I haven't any more time—."

He was up without formality. "Review the same lesson with Father X Wednesday; that's your next time, isn't it? He'll be back then."

Father X explained Hope . . . "by which we trust God will give us eternal life and the means to get it. By the grace of faith, we naturally are led to hope for a restoration of what our first parents lost for us. And we try to work for it. So we pray for help to get us over the whispering work," and he smiled, "of Lucifer and his crowd, and against our human inclination to go the other way. Also, we try to apply the teachings, the Commandments; finally, we have the help of our Mother. And through the Church we draw practical strength by example of others and through sacraments and other aids, receiving Jesus Himself within ourselves, reinforcing us against the pull of the world we're exiled in. The final goal is, of course, reunion with God, who sent us. And by helping others and trying to see through eyes of goodwill and forgiveness—*really* trying—we get the rush of help itself, the helping hand of Jesus from the cross."

And by the sharp pain in his heart and the tenderness that rushed over him, Joseph understood the image of Weariness that had stunned him with an embrace, when they gave that thirsting loneliness a sponge.

He thought he understood the browser and the churchstep in the drizzle. And the swordthrust.

Went on Father X, "We call that grace of feeling for our neighbor, Charity. It's all Christianity in one word, the thing

God longs most to find. Hope then grows to be part of the day."

Hope suggested a goal. Suddenly it was a direction, a road.

And it stretched itself out across the wonder of his view, a faint thread glimmering, to lose itself in the far mist . . . the thing he had lacked.

The priest gave him a pocket prayerbook to keep, and a string of rosary beads which, he said, had been blessed to send grace to the user;—it would be as if the Mother Mary, whenever his fingers closed on the beads, "had come to take you by the hand." For they were her beads.

And he kept them with him always, falling asleep with them crushed in his hand to this day . . . son of Assunta and the wonder-glow.

Chapter V

THE THING EACH CONVERT MUST FACE

Joseph was aware of the new world building itself, shaping up within him. What he did not understand was that in a pagan house he was suddenly bringing home a Christian stranger, himself.

But before the two worlds could clash, something solidified deep within, steadying him.

What he was aware of was the Church, laying itself before him. And because it seemed to answer something that he had sought in that boulder desert, he tried to examine it with all prejudices set aside. But this threw all the heavier a responsibility on the fragment of critic within; he went to extremes; there were moments when he so suspected himself that in the middle of kneeling he would get up and go out, because he found himself talking within himself to silences beyond the rail.

But there were times when he could feel so mired there before the Cross and its mother, that he could not look up . . . and would find his head in his hands on the rail. One day tears blurred his eyes there; he found himself rubbing his fingers across his eyes to dry them. And touching the wet finger to the nail through the two feet of the image before him, he heard himself saying, "I'm sorry for my nail; these are probably not real tears; but take them;—does it feel better?"

As he walked out, self-suspicion must have started to call this to his attention, because he suddenly said, "I don't give a damn if it *was* delusion. I feel better."

Of the fight with himself that is indicated, here is another flash, in a letter written to Father Mac the purser, at the end of an empty interlude, but never mailed; it was dated June 28 (1934), and it says in part:

DEAR FR. MC——,

There was nothing pressing in those calls I made on you—always at the wrong time; I'd have bothered you—you're so good, to bother. I thought I wanted to report.

Put right to it, I don't know what I wanted to report. I've never been honest with myself. When you've been capable of a dishonest use of talents, you rip at your sudden show of piety. Will a liar believe himself?

Suppose it turns out just one more self-glorification? . . . I must be careful to be honest with you, and the God you teach me; I mustn't spoil this, I'm afraid I can . . . I'm giving myself so intently that I fear finding myself merely earnestly hypnotizing myself, wanting beauty. But I don't know; that's why I tremble.

I walk the fourteen stations to Calvary, and kneel when He falls with the cross, and find myself praying for pagans like myself who thrust a pike through Him. That I don't understand. I see Mary . . . and hear my own plea to be Galahad again, swinging for womanhood—and this stabs me weeping there. I feel the nails going through and plead punishment for having driven them, when I was born 1900 years later. . . .

I don't know, Father—I'd cursed Jesus . . . and now this Godliness. . . . Don't you see?

It's not enough to recite prayers—prayers at rising, Maria Regina's so beautiful Angelus at morning, noon and twilight; prayers at bedtime, and in between as often as I feel God—you can do that in self-delusion too.

It certainly won't be enough, to pass tests and be admitted to the bar of Confirmation; I've passed tests before, and found the cause fallen off me. It won't be enough, to be accepted for a so-holy convert by strangers, and find old friends sneering, "Since when is *he* so holy?"

How much a Catholic, a Christian, am I behind this ritual? I've recited words before—and turned out just a parrot.

I want to know, am I sincere?—I must know! But nobody can help me know that but myself; and I don't know how to make a start; this is my first try at proving myself.

I hang on Father X's lips as the sweet story unfolds; but you don't know how I long to be in the faith so earnest in his face. . . . But that critic snaps at me from within: "Ah, how do you know you believe?"

Days that I don't walk the fourteen stations I hang up the rosary beads on the electric bulb, in the dark of my bedroom, and I pray the stations there, pray for the grief of penance to stab me again, hoping to see my Lady's white face and hear her say, "Pray!—you ought be on your knees the rest of your life." For I smash her Catholic life, then briskly babble prayers to the same God.

I've brought my wife who bore the unbearable for me, to bitter tears; I have knocked my small son against the wall because suddenly a fool must render an account of the children he'd never fathered before; and she raining fists on my chest. "You damn' Wop—keep your hands off them!—don't you dare—!" . . . when a man would be as his father, teaching respect to children—or setting up a sudden God by special legislation;—what *do* we do? These Gods wreck a house that's wrecked enough. . . . And I keep praying this quiet God to charge anything I taught her to my account, transfer her burden of it to me—and suddenly that's why I'm going up that too-hard path. And, Father, is this faith?—has it really come to me? This road is unbearable every day,—it's so much more pleasant to go the other way; it's so much kinder on people you love, *not* to bring conversion home. . . .

Somewhere up the path, will I know whether belief has come? It would be so rotten to find it just sheer emptiness, longing to believe.

But I'm going on up. And if I've wandered up without ever knowing whether it was faith, and find Jesus standing there, I'd want to look up somehow with final honesty: "I wanted to profess You, but loved myself more" . . . and wait to be thrown down the stairs.

Behind all his flushed dignity-and-wires, reacting for me, Father X is in my heart to stay, whatever the outcome of this last effort. And consider the small gratitude, that I tell you instead of him. For which may he forgive me and continue to love the spirit he says is in me.

Faithfully yours,
JOSEPH TIRED

It is a hard job, trying to report a convert path that splits through a house. Here's another, written in the stillness after nerves are short-circuited by the suddenness of a fool. She had gone to a hospital again, peace all shattered:

DESERT HIGHWAY

(Two Strangers)

We are two:
A sensitized boy, son of a sensitized man
Who would be his mother before he has learned to be his father.
Mom is lying on a relief cot again
Because one of us is a fool.
Her cross
Is a double one aged Thirty-four and Thirteen;
Ah, the trial of it!
Bearing her down because two strangers
Must snarl across resentment in her kitchen
While lesions try to heal.
She'll be saying there in cot torpor:
"Who'll stand between them—now?"

I called him in—
There was something amiss,
Something needed teaching about duty
To God knows what;
Something from the ache when sons, aged Thirteen,
Or Ninety-three,
Damn a father's stewardship, most of all
By letting him down.

He came in,
Obedient and prepared to stand by, again,
For another measuring
Against something about accountability,
Something torturing a tyro, who would follow

But knows not where—
Knowing only that, once again (with a weary shrug on it)
He has been found wanting.
Some chore
In our Momless kitchen,
Assigned to him by himself
In our share-and-share agreement
Had been left undone.
And a neighbor came, and saw, and did it
In the tired brisk way
Of neighbors who look in, and stay
To give a hand. . . . I sprang up from a chair
And he came in
To stand by for a thud of hurtling words
That must drive a father's light into one's young
Or smash him.

"Get some paper and ink—
And write down: That someone had to knuckle down once more, by God!—to do a thing that you
Got out of doing!
And keep that paper
Where you'll have it every day before you—
And know yourself!"

And seeing
The rebel barricaded in his face
Even as he moved
In the trying rôle of being his father's son,
I rocked him with a whack across
The mouth;
And because eyes glared

Across the rebel stinging in the mouth
As he stood by
I snapped out, "Take that blaze off your face!"

He stooped and picked the fallen paper up,
And in the silence of a son he turned to go
And write the paper.

But because behind the slap-latticed flush the mouth
Was still a buttoned-something,
Cold fingers stilled my heart; I saw
A stranger whom I was losing—
My boy—
Whom I'd but meant to teach
From the God I found
In an atheism
That kept my first-born thirteen years an infidel
Unbaptized and strange—
Unanswered and apart—
Broody and beautiful—
A rebel. And lashing out again I snarled,
"It's still there!"
And slapped that mouth . . . and still
He stood there
Looking at me.

"Take it off!" I burst . . . and rocked him
With a third that staggered him;
But recovering his balance he moved
From the side of the neighbor against whom he had landed—
A neighbor muted in the pallor of contempt,
Her eyes a flashing whip.

And this time
Over the tremble of his buttoned mouth,
Too proud to cry
And let his father down before another,
His eyes sought mine
With tears whipping across the despair of ever knowing
What fathers want;
And he stood there to be commanded still.

His dumb hunger stabbed me.
"My God, sonny," I blurted—
And pressed him blindly in the daze of tears to my side
Dumbly
The first time I had pressed him thus in years—
It felt so good—it damned me in those tears.
"My God—," I blurted, "the way I'm driving you from me, instead of teaching—
I'm not your enemy, Boy,—I'm your father—
Try to understand."

And with these damned words stumbling
Over jangled wires—and God—and duty
I felt the lost flesh of my flesh
In an arm against my side;
And a wet upgaze
Over a trembly slap-flushed mouth said simply:
"I do, I always did."

And in that disMommed kitchen
Only the Weariness, and that
Crucified,
Beholding Adam and son

Groping together again in dust over the desert
Could possibly understand
The lame
Carrying the blind.

There is a gap indicated, between June and December in these two papers, as far apart as the seasons themselves. In one, an inquirer finds himself dazed on his knees before Calvary and rosary beads, hung from a light bulb; in the other, atheism is dazed to find itself the snarling steward of his son, teaching "God knows what" from the sudden God he would serve . . . while the mother he had poorly served must go to a hospital, for peace.

A miscarriage is obvious. A man comes home with the only thing men have found which, myth or no, can give good for evil; an atheist brings home God, and makes family life unbearable. And this does not jibe. Nor do we need to seek far for the destroying factor. It comes home in the convert.

The factor of unbearability is himself, making his world over, when in that world are others, who thus are overturned.

The new world had completely evolved within Joseph's consciousness. But he was not yet aware that he was a citizen of a re-made world—into which he must fit the old.

He saw it through this slit in the veil that Father X gave him: "Christ instituted two means by which we might share in the Redemption, getting back the garden lost through our first parents—the Church, and her Sacraments."

And he saw the Church was a band of men existing all over the world; Christ in it was the thread, connecting each member with all the rest, so that each felt whatever gladness or harm visited any part of the band. This gave rise to prayers: when some corner of it was being stoned, the band all prayed for steadiness to hold the line there; when some fragment was slipping away from Christ, the band prayed grace to give it something to grip to; when physical distress struck, the prayer was for strength with which to weather the storm, also for human charity to give a hand there.

He saw this band arrayed in three divisions. One was the present on earth, carrying on behind Christ, or, The Church Militant. The second was detained in Purgatory, till the last stain of disobediences that had been repented of should burn away; this was The Church Suffering. The last, the goal of all the band, was reunion with the Father, Son and Holy Ghost, or God, in the garden whence life had come. This was the seat of the kingdom spoken of by the Son; here He was King, His mother Queen, the angels the court, the saints the advocates pleading our cause together with the Mother He had given us. The Mother Mary was the first and last to plead for us, the Christians, who became her children, the mother who, through Christ, was become again, Eve, interceding for her exiled children. And this final phase was The Church Triumphant.

The same thread connected each division of the band; the living thread was the same Christ. And Joseph saw one world in three sections all living, and a fourth section also living, called hell, where stilled people lived, sentenced by uncharity and a living that had been anti-Christ unrepented, to be separated from God through all eternity.

He saw no physical suffering in this fourth state of life,

but he could sense a hell of silent anguish, such as he had felt in desert boulders in the anguishing memory of a breeze from some far garden, making the empty desert more empty still.

He found himself searching backward in that four-division world, for the beginning of the band of Christians carrying this vision to him and he received this account of the band who outlived Rome, unfolded by Father X.

"To them Calvary was very real," said Father X, "an eye-witness story carried from father to son.

"Two things stand out in the accounts carried down to us from generation to generation through Christ who guides this continuity. These two things are the humanity that could face death in the most violent forms, and that could feel Calvary so much that they had to *express* that sorrow and personal shame, when they realized that the Son of God had died because He wanted to draw them back home.

"On one side we see a powerful nation, ruler of the entire civilized world, unable to stamp out so weak a band, whose membership meant getting a sword through you. Or else the persecutors poured oil and you were set on fire in the streets, or they broke your teeth with pincers, one by one, cut parts of you off, shamefully desecrated you if you were a rich or important woman, threw your children under horses or into the fire, before your eyes—anything to break down your silence when they wanted you to say you were for the established gods. We see all this torture and death, inflicted singly or wholesale in public, to teach what it meant when you abandoned the gods and defied Caesar; yet we find the answer always the same: Christ; and Him crucified. And yet the scattered, fear-shaken survivors always gathered again somewhere to hear some successor to the apostles renewing Calvary and the message again, with more listeners to take the place of the dead, and more raiders breaking through to drag them before the authorities. Yet Rome wasn't able to stamp it out.

"In fact—and here's the other side of it—we see a death-haunted human association meeting in catacombs and huts and other places, wherever a converted citizen offered room, to hear the epistle of the successor to Peter, and listen to the local leader of the group, and receive the broken bread and wine, and sponsor new converts with baptism, or join two in marriage by the new rite, or offer prayers to bury them, and other prayers for thanks, for sorrow, for a plea for light for fellowmen, for all the reasons for which men and women shaken by the Redeemer still pray today. And we see candle services, and holy-day services, and services for the martyred, and services for Mary Intercessor, and occasions for devotion and prayer, with fast, penance, joy—the beginning of a liturgy growing, expanding, compacting, and becoming suddenly public, to march chanting with torches or candles right out in the Roman streets, so much were they moved to give public expression to the feelings awakened by sight of the Son of God who because of His love for man could die so shamefully.

"And seeing these outbreaks of open demonstration so dear to the Roman heart, Rome did not know what to do. These were her sons and daughters, her soldiers, statesmen and citizens, also slaves, Easterners and Jews, all ranks leveled, all banded as one, for One; these were her children. This was

Rome herself. Suddenly, this was man himself, clumsily trying to reach to the Creator who had suddenly shown love and forgiveness,—shown a personal affection for His stranded children.

"Rome saw her legions swarming down to hack at the procession till the streets ran red and torches spat out in blood; then she saw the same soldiers joining the next chanting procession. It was useless. Going on knifing, burning and dissecting them, she was killing *herself*. Then suddenly the emperor himself carried the cross—and the whole legion with him. The empire looked the other way and, finally herself professed God in Christ. And Christianity triumphed . . . as, of course, Christ had predicted. He had stayed with the weak band, against which neither man nor hell was to prevail, for He had promised to be with the band around Peter always. He had warned of desertions and open schism, revolt and the springing-up of sects and of attractively presented pictures by apostles who would mislead many from the flock; but He would abide by the flock always, with the warning that for His sake it would be persecuted to the end; for He would be there. All of this has happened; and you'll find out, if it works out that you become a Catholic, that there's still persecution for His Church; if you were standing by her today, in Mexico and Russia, and maybe Spain, it might mean death."

The priest went on, "The Church still gathers the faithful round Christ, holding Mass and carrying on the liturgy out of the catacombs and confessing penitents to give them Christ in the Sacraments, visibly, to help us live good lives invisibly. And it's the invisible part, the kingdom itself, that most marks the faithful and is least acknowledged in the world—the lifting of the human self as an offering to God, so often the only thing we have to give—the prayers for our fellow-men not of the flock—the prayers and self-denials for the departed—the little man's effort to fight his own temptations and really try to obey God, submitting to the Church on the authority of His Word, going to her as to Jesus' Mother, and going from her into the street to try to obey and forgive as best he can. It's in the invisible daily church that the Catholic is acknowledged least, while his faithful liturgy and changelessness are attacked. In the invisible world, too, the Mother, Church, is betrayed most by her own people because in the Kingdom of Christ you can't serve self and pretend to serve God. So if our trust is so great because Christ passes it on to us, our responsibility is correspondingly great—and betrayal all the more hurts Him when it's by one of the faithful.

"The Church has come through the centuries, the only thing of this world to endure man's blight. In a world of change, unrest and unauthority in which at best everything gropes with the problems of the moment, the Church of the universal or catholic band remains steadily the same;—I don't know if you have ever thought of that, or, if you have, whether you saw something accidental, some ritual happening to live because it was clever enough not to change. But we must remember that precisely because it *wouldn't* change, and wouldn't swing over when a shift might seem expedient, is exactly the reason why all generations have tried to overthrow it, or at least discredit it. Hacked at and burned, abandoned and outlawed, attacked on all sides by pagans and schisms, and betrayed again and again by her own, she goes on, offering the other cheek. Christ Himself, raising the cross over the daily world, drawing a band—a band now as it was in the days of the Coliseum, giving the same message from the same Authority, and guarding the only practicable road of peace from the cradle on to Him Who sent us. Do this: think of the twenty centuries trying to overthrow it and its changeless face in spite of all attack and change. Then some day ask yourself: could it really be, that Christ *is* abiding with it so that nothing can prevail against it?"

It *did* strike Joseph.

One other thing rose up before him: the present burning of priests in oil in Spain, the slaughter of peons at church doors in Mexico when with arms crossed over breasts they refused to stand aside for the soldiers of radicalism, the hunting of priests in Russia who escaped the general proscription, the stonings in Scotland. The general cry was, "Away with ignorance; break the priestcraft that chains the masses and bars the State; away with the Pope!" But as an atheist it leaped across his mind, that when atheism struck, it struck not at Christendom but at the cross, not at temples but at the Catholic Church; it struck universally at a known mark: Rome; the atheist knew where faith was. "Also," he reflected, "one religion or form might condone or ignore or debate with the other; but all would like to see Rome burn."

Joseph dumped the stones out of his pocket on the ground and decided, "If a man worships at all, be it a moon or a cow, an idol or God in any form, I want to shake a good man's hand; he sees something better than himself and tries to acknowledge it."

The continuity of the Christians began to move across his

whole consciousness. He was, without knowing it, seeing Christ in all things, man trying to give himself to God.

He felt the pulse of it in the little pocket prayer-book. It contained much liturgy from the centuries, outpourings of the human heart, all the effort of that heart to sustain the pressure of the moment in its attempt to serve God . . . the tremendous attempt of little man, crying out with weariness and yet trying to climb up over rocks. The pilgrim's progress.

He suddenly loved this little book of inarticulate man. He loved it for its anonymity, for its shabby human heart, offering clumsy roses and pleading to be lifted from the rocks; he loved it for the fight of man despairing of climbing them, when he longed to go down and buy a harlot a beer instead. He saw the man who lives near by, dumping a handful of wages into a cripple's cup, staggering home to face his wife and have the door banged in his face again . . . and be quietly stirred awakening on the darkened lawn, to be helped into the house where two will try to be one once more, bearing each other's crosses: one-in-two, Eve's Adam.

They were all in that little book. He learned the meaning of silence in a bristled face, waiting before the confessional on Saturday, where the first century had knelt behind uneasy Roman power. It was all here in broken passages, man's ghastly failure—gallant man, trying again, once more, to fall once more. Here was the *understanding* God, that other side of Him, perhaps wearily watching the lipsticked and the shaven penitents who had all been here before—beholding that seamy earth-stained other side of the White-robes who at the pinch would tremblingly stand up and die for the faith again. The booklet gave to Joseph what he absolutely needed: an understanding of the human failure behind the effort to reach up to God; he had to find behind the ideal the realism of man, staining grace with self, and yet rising above himself.

Here are some fragments from Joseph's prayer-book:

"Here I cast myself at Thy feet: consider not in what manner, at what time, or how late: consider only that I come. But ah! Lord, in how miserable a condition!"

"Hear me speedily, O Lord: my spirit hath fainted away."

"Who am I, O God of glory and Majesty! who am I that Thou shouldst deign even to look on my unworthiness?"

"Eternal Power! Adorable Holiness! My soul longs to annihilate itself before Thee."

"Behold the handmaid of the Lord: do with me as Thou wilt."

"Mystical Rose . . . Gate of Heaven . . . Morning Star . . . Refuge of Sinners . . . Queen of the Rosary . . . and of Peace: pray for us."

"Hail, Holy Queen, Mother of mercy, our life, our sweetness and our hope; to thee do we cry, poor banished children of Eve . . . weeping and mourning in this valley of tears."

"Permit me then, O Lord, to join my feeble voice with the host of heavenly spirits; and to exclaim with them, in transports of joy, 'Holy, Holy, Holy, Lord God of Sabaoth, the heavens and the earth are filled with Thy glory."

And the rosary, the beautiful rosary . . . roses woven to the mother of the cross, receiving children's prayers for Him, each bead a rose. It is sweetest in the cracked old voice of grandma, making the bouquet once more.

And . . . the flower . . . by the sign of which a man has tried to carry on.

Here's a paper on it, that began as a letter to Father X and grew into another beginning of that futile Report; the first page is lost:

"How is a man harmed who considers a bit of beauty? We have mud always with us.

"Something has more than once stopped me, with senses quivering, all steeped through with a stab of perfume, as if a shifting breeze had brought the fragrance of a rose garden, and every fibre wanted to drink—throw itself in and drink of the freshness.

"I was walking, with the memory of trouble at home over God, and over a night's useless writing that I had torn up again, up the convert path, the other day. I suppose I was tired; I know I was ready to quit the effort to write of the road to God, when God must split a wedge through my house, smash my wife's tired nerves, and earn me a woman's revolt, because a fool must set up the God he had broken in her, and himself not sure whether he can accept Him or us.

"And while wearily kneeling before the image of the Bosomful of Roses, finding emptiness in me I stood up to go out, aware of the futility, and sick of the wasted reams of writing on it. Then seeing the guide of the effort entering the chapel with a simple smile, I went in there to report the useless writing and the empty gesture of kneeling, that had begun to seem God in me at first.

"She said I was tired; it wasn't Deity teaching me penance by twisting all my works and all my report out of hand. But after a pause she said, 'But it is. Why does He twist the effort to write a report on *this*, though?' To which I had no answer.

"Then she asked if I had ever tried praying St. Thérèse to take up my case; she had been wholly devoted to God while alive, with such longing to see us all restored in heaven that miracles followed after her death.

"I had never heard of Thérèse. She said, 'But you always kneel at her image.'

"Then it turned out that this was the statue of the Bosomful of Roses, where for six months I had prayed, thinking the image represented my Virgin Lady.

"And I grew sick.

"'That just about sums up the convert I've been,' I remember muttering; 'it's on a level with the rest of the things I've messed.'

"There sat a silence on us both, and I saw that she was troubled. She quietly said, 'Mother Mary will understand that, and did from the start; there must be a reason why God allowed the mistake to continue—and why *she* did. She must have wanted you to have St. Thérèse; certainly six months ago when you first looked at her image something must have drawn you to her.'

"'The beautiful youth of her,' muttered Joseph.

"'Something more.'

"Then she told me the story of St. Thérèse, the young

holiness of whose face had first drawn me. And the sheer loveliness of the story held me mute.

"It concerns a girl and roses, who so loves people, that she made her youth a prayer, which she offered for us, that we see the Jesus she loved so. She became a nun, and her child-like faith and patient victory over self, her daily Christianity in small things, her heroic suffering in her illness—but most of all her burning love of Jesus, were to be quickly raised as the model of sainthood for the man-in-the-street. When desperate illness choked her one night, she ran counter to human nature; nobody young and beautiful wants to die; but she burst into tears of wonder. Jesus wanted her. With simplicity she stated she was to continue working for us, making her heaven an intercession for us through Jesus. If the need is pressing, I was told, and faith in her power strong enough, the response of Jesus is already won. That was her message. And the sign that His help was to come would be a flower; someone least expected would bring a flower. And when from all ends of the world arose reports of favors received, the Church investigating found evidence of cures and answers not explainable by natural law and gave to the world at the turn of the present century a new saint. —A remarkable thing: a girl's sainthood established because of humble chores and answered prayers—and announced within a generation after her death. It often takes three hundred years of investigation before a saint is established. The world was electrified; one false step in 'declaring' a saint must surely smash Catholicity. Yet here she stands, by the cross, honored in all nations by Catholics and non-Catholics, and not a lifetime dead. Thérèse, nun of France; died, aged about twenty-three, after completing the autobiography the Church commanded her to write. St. Thérèse of the Holy Face and the Child Jesus. They stand her movingly beautiful likeness near the kneeling rail, by the cross. The Little Flower. Either the world's millions who speak her name are deluded, or—But, the beauty of it—

"A flower, for sign!

"And if the whole thing be but a flower, consider: men have raised a flower, by which to draw themselves out of the bog.

"And if I hung in the hearing of it, suspended between whether to see a garden in it or a legend softening a desert of stones, who'll damn me for longing to breathe perfume?

"I might have known only boulders."

St. Thérèse had swept him off his feet.

The guide said she knew a woman who had received the sign, when given up to die; her swift recovery remains a local byword. The ex-secretary, contemplatively sitting in the chapel pew, seemed lost in wonder. She presently went on to disclose that she herself had asked a sign of The Little Flower, without result, either because her need was not great enough, or her faith in the nun not absolute enough. "I have an idea yours wouldn't waver a hair; why don't you ask her whether to go on with the report?"

He would try it. She said an informal novena of prayer had sprung up in the street; it ran twenty-four days. On each day a short set prayer to the sainted young nun was said, to be followed immediately after by the Glory prayer, repeated twenty-four times. She looked in her bag but found she had left the leaflet at home. "But you could make up your own petition, and followed with the Glories,—to be continued through the whole twenty-four days," she advised, "whether you get the sign or not."

She left him and he wondered what to do. If it was again a testing of his response, it was a hard one; a beautiful story is one thing, a prayer to a dead nun for a flower, another.

The error that he had made laid weariness on him when he went to kneel by the cross, before the young dignity which, for six months, he had known as that of the mother, Mary. Over this futile feeling swept an awareness of his structure of filth, that had struck at all this beauty. Then through it struck the loneliness nailed above him with arms outflung.

His gaze wanted to lower at memory of the dare flung up at this inoffensiveness; somehow it could not. He found it lifting as if longing to find someone to speak for him, and it fell on the cleanly young dignity profiled there, roses crushed to her breast. "What mud I bring," he thought; "she crushes roses to her to endure my kind."

Then trying to feel contact somewhere with a troubled nun urging men to hold on harder, he burst out, "I know I oughtn't be kneeling here, contaminating you; I never even heard of you, and came before your image all this time, thinking it was Mother Mary; that gives you an idea of what I am. . . . I suppose I came here so much because you're beautiful; but your story has brought me now; I'm grateful for it, it was like a garden. I believe you've got the power, St. Thérèse, and that if you say the word I'd get a flower. I wanted to know whether to go on writing that report or not, it gets twisted all the time. I'll go through with the twenty-four days, just the same. It was good just to have heard the story. Thank you for it. And if you'll tell Him I'm sorry—"

He shook his head. "What a twist of a prayer," he thought; and seeing the drooping Carpenter slung before him he murmured, "Pray for us, Holy Mother of God, that we may be made worthy of the promises of Christ. And may the souls of the faithful departed rest in peace, Amen." He felt better now. And beginning the repetition of the Glory prayer, he soon found he must furtively count on his fingers joined before him, having never learned to memorize a continuity. This made him feel more uneasy still. But he finished the prayer twenty-four times and rose up, saluted with the quick military salute he used for the Carpenter when no one was there to see, and got in the car to ride to Bureau Headquarters, for there was to be a meeting of relief agents.

And as he stepped into the smoke-filled room of the war-veteran agents, Jess the gum-chewer came to him and pinned a blood-red flower on Joseph's lapel, saying, "You're our delegate to Mae West. Here's your credentials, the flower."

Joseph without waiting for the meeting to which they had been summoned rode across the county to Father X, to whom he quietly gave the flower. . . . He examined it with wonder.

"It's—great! So beautiful, and strange; it's like dripping blood," with wonder murmured the priest. He added, "I never saw this kind before, where did you get it?"

"From The Little Flower, St. Thérèse; but I don't ask you to believe that."

Then Joseph told him that he had just heard the story, and explained the confusion of images, and the petition for a flower for sign. "I have no right to say it's a sign," he said quietly, "but I'm going on with the writing, on the strength of it. In all my life, it's the first flower anyone ever gave me, except one that a girl threw to me when we marched in from France. And it was given me by a hard-faced man, a soldier, who had a garden full and brought a vase full to give to our new supervisor, a woman they sent down to our mob of men; he didn't give a flower to anyone else; men don't give flowers to men—or soldiers don't. A half-hour after asking a sign, I walk in and he pins this on me saying, 'You're our delegate to Mae West; here's your credentials, the flower.' I stood still. My guide, the young woman, had told me it would be casually given but in an absolutely unexpected way, with some words that would say, 'This is for you.' I wanted to make sure he meant it for me personally, and not at random in that crowd. I asked him if he meant it for me. He said, 'Sure. It's your credentials.' I asked him again, if he meant it personally for me. He said, 'I gave it to you, didn't I?' Then he went to his desk and set to work, chewing gum absent-mindedly. I was stunned standing there; why, I don't know, except that in another way Jess had told me, 'This is the sign.' I went to him and said the third time, 'I've got to be absolutely sure. You meant this for me? You had it in mind for me when I came in?' Jess likes me, because, I think, of the fight I made the first day for someone who was marked down. He looked up surprised and annoyed at this question asked so many times. He said, '*I* brought those flowers; I got them out of my yard, they're mine. I guess I can give one to whoever I want, can't I?' I had embarrassed him and they were staring at me."

"I have heard about the sign, of course," said the priest,

"and of some people who received it. But this is the first time I have held one that had come to someone." He gazed with wonder at the flower in his hand. It was a tall-stemmed, gracefully tapered flower, vividly fresh. He repeated, "Like blood. It's very strange, and very beautiful; I never saw one like it. But I don't know enough about flowers to know their names—all I know is that I love them." He gave the flower back to Joseph.

Joseph made no move to take it. He said, "I bring it back where it came from. Keep it, from me."

The priest was glad. On impulse Joseph asked for a part of the plant to keep. He broke off a small side-flower whose petals had been lost.

The dried husk is folded in his little pocket prayer-book to this day. It really has helped him.

Joseph found trouble at home, where his wife was not well, and he found he gave her offense.

The offense was that a stoner of her faith should babble on his knees, under rosary beads dangling from the light bulb. Within himself he was walking the stations to Calvary, but inconstancy will silence a man. Pledging his spirit to God, he whacked his son's head off. He probably dangled the truth of God down through the evening until her nerves jangled. He must man the barricade and raise the cross every time that kin or visitor said or did something not Christian. "For *God's* sake will you *please* shut up?" she had to plead; "it's God, God, God till I'm sick of it."

He shut up.

Walking the stations round church walls he would urge

again, "Put her burden all on me; I put it on her, it's mine." She had gone down to the little surgical door three times to face the darkness and come back or be carted away, alone. She was failing again. Just when he should comfort her he must pound her with the Deity. "Give me a hand, I don't know where I'm at," he begged down the church wall.

There was another jolt in instructing his son again. "I'll teach you to respect your elders and your obligation in this world, if I'm hated to the end for it," he burst in a crash of reaction. A mother's resentment flared up. And seeing the effort to teach all snarled up again, he jumped up from supper and sent his coffee cup shattering against the wall . . . and wandered down night streets, unable ever to get a grasp on himself, with tears breaking loose and a woman on a porch staring at him going by. To end it all he might better give up the God experiment and be a father again; how was it that you hurt only your little world of love, the only thing you want? He wandered till late, he saw he was far . . . and turned again, Whittington, Lord Mayor of nothing.

She was still standing where he had left her by the broken peace of the supper table, with her limp young arms and weary face. She must have cried and cried; he saw the wretchedness of loneliness in the trembling hunger of the face turning to his, and in her quiver-lipped "Dood,—"

"Ah, Dood, hell," he huskily said, "you ought to kick me down the stairs." He wandered in past her silent look; the splash of coffee on the wall met his eyes over the broken pieces of cup on the floor. This was the man who had found beauty unutterable, in a white-robed band of God. Where had they put it? It had been in him. Where did it all go?

He leaned his back against the wall, all adrift in a twisted everything, all lost. He blurted, "*I* don't know where it goes, —everything I touch gets blighted—you don't know the plan I had, nobody does;—this wasn't it."

Tears blurred out the kitchen. "This isn't what I planned, —a rat-hole in a provincial town—whacks for my son—Ruth doesn't ask for her pony any more—. Plans—. A streetcleaner from Italy can put up a house with a piano and a washing machine and love for his bunch—and make it home with his peace;—it doesn't take a fine mind for that,—what good is a mind?—it betrayed me," he told the blur of tears before him. "I wanted only truth, it's beautiful—and I smash my house with it—I don't even know how to keep God from going to pieces in my hands;—it's about time something stopped me from trying to run *anything*—it would be kindness to this family, before I smash it past fixing up—."

He leaned against the wall, a castaway adrift alone; all the world was flooded in bright blurry water. Across it afar bobbed three faces, two little ones beneath the bigger one, huddled there, on a reef. The front one rose up, white, ugly, distorted, tear-washed, the mother-face, its quivering mouth drawing the face all awry, the two smaller faces stunned one to either side of it; it had been beautiful before.

"That's right, stare," he blurted, "rip me down with your dumb faces—look at a first-class failure;—but you'll never know I went down there against myself, to look for something to make myself over, for you—all you see is the mistakes; nobody'll ever see the inside of me in a thousand years; —I'm standing alone—." Wabbly lips wouldn't form words any longer.

He found himself in his mother's rounded white peasant arms; they sank him within their soft warmth so fragile and yielding, he could cry in the closet and sleep a week now. Dumb hands felt his back . . . the slim arms of the Luna girl tightened around him. She understood a man needed hiding from himself. Across his blurred gaze in her arms, she told him it was all right, they were back together again, it was all right; she smiled to assure him. Then she burst into tears. "I don't know where we—"

She didn't know where they'd drifted to.

Then quietly he had her in his arms.

"It's all right," he said, "we're home."

CHAPTER VI

THE PASSING OVER

HIS inquiries went on. Mother Church had grown dearer. He had suffered a burn for her.

He had broached the subject of baptizing the children and of transferring them from Dr. A.'s charge to the Catholic Church. They could talk now of God, a little. But she had at once flared up. "I knew it! I was waiting for it— They'll stay right where they are. I'm through with *your* proposing and *our* following and getting burned."

"I thought—"

"Sure,—*you* thought. The whole world has to stop and listen, while you start another experiment. Go on and be a Catholic. But you leave the children to me; they're mine; you made me suffer for them. You stuck them into a church that walked out from the church God made. Well, they're there now and they'll stay. But you had the nerve to ask *me* to join the unfaithful."

"Then why did you go?"

"I didn't go to a church, I followed you."

The swiftness left him absolutely mute. Here was woman, obeying Genesis: cleave to thy man.

The troubled face of Father X reviewed this.

"She suffered perhaps more than you'll know. Your first

duty is to bring peace at home. No occasion for more suffering."

He told Joseph his only course lay in quiet Christian example, and prayer. "It must be another cross He imposes on you. Now that you want Him at home you are deprived of that peace. Pray to Our Mother to take charge, for your wife and for you."

He prayed to Mary . . . and to Joseph, the sainted kindly man who so clumsily, so humbly looked at the God-child his wife had borne under circumstances odd enough to earn her being condemned to death. Instead he fathered this unknown child born in a stable with what dignity circumstance allowed. The man Joseph quietly accepted both the woman and her son. How he must have borne stares, going around asking food for a woman with child in a stable; and possibly his fellow-villagers guffawed behind his back.

Here was the universal woman's-man, a man standing by.

"Joseph, St. Joseph," urged the convert kneeling by the imaged Kindliness-in-a-niche, "take charge of another father."

He told the priest, "For my Confirmation and the Christian naming, if I come out a believer at the end, I would like to have the name of St. Joseph. In my enlistment for Christ, if he'll take back a deserter, I'd like to be assigned to some desert outpost, the last one. I'll try to stand by the Holy Family for Joseph, there."

In that last outpost, the desert of oneself.

He began to attend Sunday Mass, as an inquirer sitting in.

Suddenly the Mass was both understandable and . . . just what the ex-secretary had said: it was beautiful.

It was in Roman to preserve both the original for all time and to make for uniformity. The Bible was its book. There were readings of Scripture each Sunday and holy-day of Mass obligation. No matter where the nation, what the tongue, how strange the peoples, the appointed Epistle and Scriptures of the day were read—the same in every Western Church in every part of the world that day—in China and Canada, South Africa and Siberia, France and Chicago and New York and Palm Beach and Scudders Landing. Nobody challenged this lack of originality; the sameness was a comfort to the woman from Belgium stranded on Sunday in Shanghai, or to the man under a derby from Brooklyn in Egypt. In the Eastern Church of the Continuity, the Byzantine Rite prevailed, the home tongue was spoken, but the visiting White-robe was at home there too, for there was Christ and Mary; and there too Peter-in-the-Pope spoke when Christ had a message. Oneness was the mark everywhere, peoples were made one by it. "If this isn't it, we'll all squat a machine on its haunches in the dust, and give ourselves to it while it neatly presses our pants. And then humbly murmur, How modern,—how beautiful!"

Father X explained, "Mass is the offering of the human nature and substance of Jesus—His body—for sacrifice on the altar, by Himself. It is the same sacrifice as the cross, except that now it is unbloody. He offers it daily with Himself as both High Priest and victim, the priest offering himself with everyone present. Jesus does this to unite us to Himself in one sacrifice, by offering the broken bread and the wine, and in fulfillment of the startling words which He told the people of Palestine: 'Unless ye eat my flesh, and drink my blood, you shall not have life (eternal) in you.'"

He continued, "It was truly 'a hard saying.' Notice that the people didn't misunderstand His direct language; they understood Him exactly, word for word, as He said it. They understood precisely what He said: that He was asking man to eat His flesh and drink His blood. This was repulsive to them. They were asked to be cannibals. They looked at one another. 'This is a hard saying,' they said. They saw that He meant it just as He said it. It was necessary to eat Him to have everlasting life. Note that He repeated it, and absolutely refused to explain how they were to accomplish this, yet expected them to be ready to do so; for this was His final and suddenly direct, unconditioned message; it upset all Palestine. 'How can this man give his flesh to eat, and his blood to drink?' But quietly He went away.

"But note again, that at the last supper, breaking bread, He said abruptly, '*This* is my body—Take ye and eat all of this; *for this is my body.*' And with the wine, 'Take ye and drink all of this; for this is *the chalice of my blood*, of the New Testament, which for many shall be shed unto the remission of sins.'

"In that we see again the direct meaning, stated deliberately and exactly. He didn't say, 'This is *as* my body,' but made a positive declaration that this now *was* His body—just as positive and short-spoken as when He said His body must be *eaten*. Suddenly He was saying *why* His body was to be eaten; this would be the continuous, daily way to receive *Him*, strengthening the weak human man with the perfect obedience and all-conquering strength of our Savior. And it was to be accomplished daily in the act of breaking the bread and dedicating the wine with the exact words and meaning left by Him.

"But *how* this bread and wine was become Himself, He left absolutely veiled. Having shown what to do and having stated the case now known as transubstantiation, by which bread becomes flesh though still seeming to be bread, He left it in mystery. And all time leaves the veil there.

"We do not know why He left this hard saying with us. It faces every convert. But doing as commanded, the apostles did it daily, and we are their successors. We are simply trying to do what Jesus commanded. And we will continue to do it as long as there's one of us left."

Something unspeakably dignified—withdrawn—majestic—passed before Joseph. He said, "I've decided,—I accept it just as it stands."

"Why?" quickly asked the priest.

"Because no invented fake would have left such a stumbling block as this hard saying—no inventor could sell it. Nobody but a God of dignity," he decided, "could put it down on the table to be accepted or not—on the authority of just His two words. That's just exactly the absolute authority I've needed."

He had to appeal very quickly to that authority. His house had come to a bad pass.

Rent came due, his wife was ragged and failing, they had to move and the furniture would suddenly collapse when they'd sit on it, it was too broken to move . . .

Because something had to be done at once, Joseph at last

jumped amidstream and did what he could in the flood—no time to think, except swiftly to ask St. Joseph to direct.

He took his wife on the relief round—why, he couldn't tell; abruptly she made him stop the car, to point at an empty house and say, "Let's take that house." They went to the city and contracted for a frugal set of new furniture, to be paid for in monthly installments. Joseph saw an official he knew at the Lighting Company, and they agreed to transfer the cooking and lighting service despite the arrears which must customarily be paid before service would be transferred elsewhere, and despite the fact that Joseph lacked the twenty dollars of new deposit-money required. Also, as a symbol of a new start, he prevailed on them to send an electric refrigerator, to be paid for at the rate of twenty-five cents a day.

The first upset in this flood plan came in selling the old furniture. A Jew offered five dollars for Joseph's possessions and grunted, "I'll junk it and make a dollar; I wouldn't put that junk in my stable." All Joseph's worth was estimated at $5. And the Jew was struck in the face by the flashing pride of the invalid wife of Joseph . . . who burst with the effort to keep his fist down, as the better part of a Christian. But Negroes and another Jew who was a housekeeper in poverty, bought the furniture between them for sixteen dollars.

Harry the car-mechanic and Joseph moved the personal belongings to the bungalow across the county down in the district where Joseph acted as relief agent. He doesn't know why they moved there or what made his wife suddenly want this so. But he thinks St. Joseph took charge, in view of what was to happen there in the end.

Eve stayed at her mother's house down there, near by during the time they were moving the few personal goods. There was a jolt again over the failure of children to mind their elders; he was charged with being a hypocrite; this invoked a father's right to teach—another rocking slap of his son's head,—and it was the final straw. In the confusion and nerves and sobs that rained blows on his breast, Joseph found himself pushed backward, staggering through her mother's door into the night, from a jangle of sobs that burst out, "Get out—get out! it's been a knife in me long enough—I don't want to see you ever again—!" And the door crashed in his face.

Harry drove the car home in the silence. Both men shared the same thought. She was breaking, fast.

He was too stunned to react and went woodenly through the intervening night and day, till with Harry he took the last goods to the new house and then went to her in her mother's house, to bring his remorse to her.

"It's all right," she said, "I may not be in the way much longer."

He replied, "That's what I feared."

No more was said. Her mother made them a silent supper.

They went to the new house next day and waited for the furniture and for the gas and electric service. They received two letters instead. They were refused furniture, for lack of security; he was only a name in the book of relief. And there would be no gas-electric service. They must pay the forty-eight dollars arrears and twenty dollars more for new service;

nor would they get the refrigerator. They did not have five dollars. They were fully washed up in the flood.

They drew the shades at night so that none could see that the house was empty of furniture. And sitting around a candle in the dark on the floor, they ate cold cheese for want of a fire in the gas stove.

And laughing, Joseph stood up and said, "I'm free—absolutely free at last; I'm washed up, flat broke, no more responsibility." He called out, "Deal the cards, Life; it's your move next."

Nobody replied to this. "I waited thirty-four years for this." He must mock himself. "How my father would congratulate me. 'I sweated blood!' he would say, 'to send you to the schools to consummate this.'" Then he stopped pacing round the walls in the candle light. In the cage it is useless to bruise your wings.

Reaction came. And the self-mockery had been easier to bear than self-pity.

"A touch from me, and it falls apart." It jangled on nerves in the candle silence. He was perhaps just bewildered. But his wife was failing again. No furniture.

"This is what I bring you to; it's not your fault—you have me on your hands;—I'm in everybody's way—"

"Ah, shut up," burst out his wife.

He checked the babble of lips. "I'm tired," he said, "try not to mind me." Harry gave him a cigarette. "No need for you to ride a sinking ship with us, Harry," he quietly said across the match they shared. Then tears gleamed in Harry's hard little eyes, surprise and pain spread across the battered face. "Dis is a fine time f' me to cut for shore," Harry said. He stood uncomfortably there. Joseph abruptly gave his shoulder a press. "All hands at stations;—stand by!" cheerily he called out, "prepare for the last heave!"

"Take it easy," anxiously urged Harry, "we'll get t'rough dis."

They slept on the floor that night.

Harry, the pagan, had not returned at dusk; he had left in the morning. Eve roused sufficiently to say quietly, "He felt he was being a drag on us." Joseph missed him, too. But Harry was to be of almost superhuman help from that hour; he had been out all day, making restless efforts to find a job, —Harry with the bald head where someone had smashed a beer bottle down.

In the morning light, Joseph reacted. Oddly, the touchstone was the refrigerator, price twenty-five cents a day. It was to have been a symbol of a new, Christian effort at homebuilding.

The estimate of the business world cut his last pride. It had marked him down. He saw his wife and children sitting on the floor. Then tears of humiliation blurred them completely away.

"Right on the nose. They took my measure. They got me on paper, hundred percent right, at last. A bum risk. N.G. Marked lousy. My friends have been pulling me through. Well," he shrugged through his tears, "it's been a long time coming. I couldn't slide through on my wonderful mind, forever. But it stings. They couldn't trust me for twenty-five cents a day. In all the world there's nobody with any intelligence at all, who'd take a chance on me for twenty-five cents."

His speech lodged in his throat; he had to suck it back with a terrible sound. "It hurts like hell—."

And he shrugged himself, with hands in his pants pockets, and a blur for vision.

Then through the blur he saw Gil the Sensitized, the dreamy-eyed and beautiful—his Rebel, aged thirteen and small. He seemed to sidle languorously around the walls, hands in pockets like his father, and a look of indifference on his face with hunger dimming his eyes. . . . Suddenly he was before Joseph with his hand out of his pocket. "*I* think you're worth it," the son said.

And trying hard not to cry he gave his father all he had —twenty-five cents for cutting Grandma's grass.

Then Ruth Eve sidled up in imitation of her brother, and put four pennies in a shaky hand. "Put this in the icebox the second day," she commanded; "but I'm only loaning you, it's *my* money."

Joseph in his Sunday suit asked his way to the credit desk in the electric-gas company.

He stated the case of a bad risk clearly, asked nothing, and put down a paper with two rows of neat figures on it. One side said how much he would earn this month. The other side said how he could pay it out. So much for new-furniture installments, so much for food, so much for rent, so much for church and household dribbles, so much for gas-electric service for the month, and ten dollars each month extra, to wipe out the forty-eight dollars deficit and establish a deposit of ten dollars for service, which he could liquidate in six months, —proposing a business deal on no money down.

"I can't ask a business man to accept this, in view of the past performance. But I can give you a better guarantee—the word of a father who has seen at last that he's the only cause of this family headache, a failure who wants to start from nothing, who can face a business man again—because my son came to me and put this quarter in my hand," he blurted out, putting the coin and the four pennies down on the desk, "when I didn't see anywhere anyone with horse-sense who could take a chance on me for twenty-five cents—and he said, 'I can take a chance on you,' and my small girl trusted me with her four cents; and," he wabbled with tumbling words, "that's my reason for coming here,—their faith,—I heard my kids say they can take a chance on their father—."

The official in a stride was up from his table and beside the overcome father, with his hand on the back of Joseph's hand. "*I'll* take the same chance, on the same faith."

"Mister—you won't regret it,—I'll see this deal through; if it breaks my back it'll be carried out by me." And it was.

The utilities company stood by the official's abrupt deal. Lights and gas came on without deposit money nor a cent of the impossible arrears; too, they sent the refrigerator, with a word of "good luck." And he publicizes this just company to this day.

On the strength of this faith in him, Joseph found a hard-pressed rural printer, who pledged his shop to guarantee Joseph's furniture, and took up the matter with another furniture house which was willing to overlook the fact of the shabby shop since it was owned by a man who would stand by his friend. "You're on relief and it's a bad risk for us—but . . . hell . . . when a decent man is stuck . . ." They rushed a houseful of furniture in the quickest shipment they could make.

But this new appraisal of Joseph moved the son of Tired.

And with all for the moment quiet, Harry at work on a small job, lights and gas on, food in the empty house, the refrigerator of the New Deal in the kitchen, the rent paid, and furniture coming, Joseph's little band found themselves holding their own.

But he thought he could see kindly St. Joseph sending the son to renew faith in his father with a sweaty small coin.

And in a corner in the empty rooms, alone, on his knees he thanked God, commending to Him His faithful St. Joseph. He stood up feeling quieted.

Going back toward the kitchen, his wife's cry of alarm brought him running. R. E. lay on the floor, doubled up in agony.

The doctor who was quickly found, ordered her taken to the hospital . . . where a consultation took place and a watch was kept, not knowing just what for. They thought it was possibly acute appendicitis but could not yet tell. Asked if there was danger, they said, "Enough."

His wife knew how deeply he felt for this placid, sing-song, humming little girl who had tired of waiting for her white pony. His wife's hand was on his. It was hot. She said quietly, "Get a priest. We'll baptize her."

He was startled. . . . Then quietly he thanked her.

The priest came hurrying. Joseph drew him aside and explained the story. It disturbed the priest. He asked whether they would mutually agree to the baptism by the Catholic Church; he must be sure, because godparents would have to sponsor the child, dying or living. They agreed. The surgeon, a Catholic, offered himself for godfather. They hurried into the halls to call for a Catholic woman. A lady passing through to visit her son, hearing the call, came up and said she was a Catholic; was there something she could do? she asked, with a graciousness that choked Joseph. She agreed to sponsor R. E., be her spiritual mother. They hurriedly consulted in search of a name for the Christ-life that was to come, and Joseph said, "Veronica." The woman of Jerusalem had wiped Jesus' face and her handkerchief was printed for reward. Joseph wound his rosary beads round Veronica's wrists. The service was said in tenseness.

Joseph, Joseph the atheist, so sure, so ready to hack at chains to free people from myths, saw two strangers, a surgeon in white coat and a sweet-faced lady in summer coolness, standing by, who had run up to insure a heaven for his baby-daughter. Tears blinded him. The priest steadily murmured on in the silence, then broke in clearly, "*I baptize thee in the name of the Father, and of the Son, and of the Holy Ghost,*" and sprinkled the water, redemption from Eve's blunder. A pagan had passed. A Christian named Veronica was born.

And, the service done, R. E. V. stirred wearily and said she wanted to go home.

Examining again, they could see nothing wrong with her, and they sent her back home.

Ruth went to Sunday School and Mass with her father every Sunday.

This was as agreed. Eve kept silence. Gil went to try a

Mass and a Sunday class. He could not understand the "show-stuff; what do they talk that foreign stuff for?" He resented the thoughtless snickerings of small boys who saw a thirteen-year-old boy sitting among the Sunday-school children. Joseph reconsidered. "Don't go to Sunday School any more. Or Mass. I'd explain the Mass, if you think you'd want me to."

But Gil began to attend with his sister. Eve did not object. Joseph spoke with Father X, back there at the north town, for he continued the convert course.

"God's hand brought Ruth through," the priest said. "It's a good sign that He's forgiving you. Your son will either follow or not. Let him alone. Pray more and set the example. Don't talk of church or God in the house. Your wife has been very, very good. Stand by her."

Gil thought he could get used to the show stuff. "It's just that I don't understand it."

Joseph asked, "Would you like to have the assistant priest explain it? I asked him about you; he seems very earnest, young, anxious to help. He'd help if you'd ask him." Gil went to see the priest. "I'm to take special instructions," he came home and said, "from the ground up. I don't know anything except hymns and commandments. I think I could like this, if I'd understand it. It feels real."

His mother did not object.

This fragment appears on a salvaged paper, telling the outcome:

"Why do I think of a son, as I sit here writing a tangled report which I keep on starting again only because The Little Flower replied, through a flower, 'Go on'—why do I think of a son? 'A little child shall lead him.' Why do I find this coming across my mind so? What are these messages from nowhere, across the troubled heart?

"He lingers with me—but gently, gently. I don't understand. He should linger roughly. A rebel sensitivity should blaze out. He lingers more gently still. I see him suddenly across sun on the morning street, taking his skippety-hoppety small sister by the hand to lead her off to the Mass. It's wonderful— He is going, sentry of a baby-faced confidence, sentry of a tenderness that instantly loved the images and the bells and the altar tableau—all the sweet face of Mother Mary, about whom she briskly instructs her dolls. He, my son, is taking my little princess to Mass, the Mass that I stoned; a little child shall lead him—. I can't understand, my head is tangled up with the script, I'm sure I want to go to bed, I'm tired— But at peace, such peace. My kids go to Mass now."

Suddenly the convert instruction was ended, the lessons were completed.

The priest of the troubled face who had fought for Joseph, stopped simply and said, "Rest a while and review yourself. Then if you're ready to make your profession of faith—"

A great daze came over Joseph, a panic, an unknowable trouble held him. Here's a preface to a new start of the report, that tells about it:

"I FEEL SURE HE
WOULD UNDERSTAND

"Yesterday a priest laid aside his catechism, six months after it was begun, and asked a question which greatly disturbs me. Because, in giving the answer truly, I shall have chosen my destiny. 'How do you feel about it? Do you think you can make a profession of faith?'

"God or paganism.

"Suddenly I realize. I am asked to surrender myself, fall on my face before Jehovah,— Can this be myself, considering such a thing?— I have been at heart all disbelief; this other must have been the hunger for beauty, grasping at unutterably beautiful straws.

"But the fact is before me. It upsets my house, amazes friends, annoys busy people who heard God too often. It rises before me now: I am a convert, considering whether to wear God.

"Friday of next week is the appointed time. I said I would be there, to announce my faith in God, before witnesses.

"But will I? There is one who suffers most by the conversion: my wife, companion of pagan rites; must I leave her standing alone? 'I didn't stop you,' she said, 'do what you see fit. But don't talk Church to me. My will is my own, it belongs to me; for once I'll think for myself. You've smashed me enough.' . . .

"Something in me wanted to take a smash in the face. This was the Catholic I had stilled.

"I wonder, wonder: do people understand they have been spared, who never suddenly confront the God of conversion? You can't look up and yet you must. Every nail burns you through; your hand feels bloody, the hammer won't go away.

"But if I don't go back, it would be because I think He

saw me in that crowd, nineteen hundred years ago, standing among the rest of us, a daub of mud in my hand to fling.

"That's why I'm afraid to go back, perhaps . . . and I must.

"This is the Introduction; we don't know how the book will start; it will be a pagan or a Christian writing it."

He seems to have made a decision right after, for we find an Introduction. Here it is:

Before the Oath

"Tomorrow a priest will be waiting to receive my profession of faith, six months from the day he opened the catechism to my atheism. He will receive my letter instead.

"I am not at all sure that he will understand—or that I do. But I am dead sure we are two disturbed men tomorrow. The six months have been a fight, almost every foot of the way; a bond of jangled sensitivities has drawn us together for life; there are some unions that can't die; burns weld them.

"I have been on the outside a hungry believer, but constitutionally opposed to any god other than myself. I have had to *know* that God is not a delusion mothered by emptiness.

"I'm sorry, unutterably sorry I wrote that letter. But let me be fair with myself: it wrote itself. I was for tearing it up. But because it was from within, I now search back for the reasons that sent that letter up out of me. For it seemed hysterical, but honest. It is absolutely the writer.

"This morning I was calm, all prepared to go tomorrow.

I *wanted* to become a Christ-follower. Then suddenly this flashed before me, and stopped me:

"I saw the garden, unexpectedly; and it was beautiful. Peace. But at the same time I saw a line of sentries, stretching down to it and they had guarded it down the generations from the Cross. They were bleeding and fearfully exhausted, but they stood; and they seemed so grimly impassable that I sensed they had delivered this peace of roses from the memory of a holocaust. And through time's veil I saw a sudden huddle of men and women, all white in the face, all shaken, but all answering steadily with one voice, 'We know no gods but Christ; and Him crucified.' Then all at once they broke screaming in all directions, oil-drenched and on fire, lighting the Roman street. The scorching crackle of them died down with the last outcry. Then over the scattered naked heaps the night closed, twilight penetrated, the dew-cool garden came back. And the line of charred sentries spoke up within the stillness in me, 'Can you hold the line against this?'

"And by the quiver of my flesh I knew the answer. I love my flesh. It is smooth and firm, it comforts me; why must I have it burned for a hard phrase?

"I saw, suddenly, that there is an obligation assumed, in being a Christian.

"China, Mexico, Spain, Russia, Germany—trouble areas of Mother Christian, the Catholic Church, baptized in blood and sprayed with it ever since,—could I, recruit sentinel, stand up in today's trouble areas and profess flames? And in the street everywhere, can I take a kick in the face, as a Popish minion? Can I stand all . . ."

That is all we can find of it.

He decided that he did not know whether he could defend the faith, come what may. But he found also that it had grown endeared to him; he fell asleep with his hand in the hand of its mother.

He wanted to know, in some reasonable way, whether for the Catholic Church he could really take that "swordthrust" of the past Good Friday.

So he wrote and said all this, proposing a test. He is a cigarette fiend; cigarettes seem fibre of his fibre. For one month he would propose to give up smoking. If he could endure the month's agony, he felt that he could offer his life to Christ.

And he thought after sending the letter, "I've lost an honest man, who believed in me. Father X will say, with my wife, with the guide of the candle, 'But this is both unnecessary and strange.' "

But the priest whose hand he had felt in hard places up the rock path, wrote swiftly back to bless this decision; he would pray for him in every Mass, commending it to Jesus.

The month began. In the remains of the diary he began to keep of the experience, we glimpse a burning fire in his senses, that longed for the solace of a cigarette. He had never gone longer than two days into experiments with giving up cigarettes; his adult life has been dotted with failures. After a day without a smoke, always by the second day (if he lasted that far) there would be a discontent smouldering. Suddenly he would walk into a cigar store and call for his brand of cigarettes. And he could expect a month of it now?

Here's a note on it, dated Sunday, Sept. 30—"No Mass this morning. Stayed abed till noon. A fire smouldered somewhere in a corner of my consciousness, it could be felt all through my fibres. The ache of that cigarette fast. . . . I don't believe it. I've gone four days without."

Here's just a line, that says a lot; dated Saturday, Oct. 7—"Eleventh day of the cross; I eat hard bread to stuff the dull fire out."

Harry urged him anxiously to "cut it out." Then after a crawling period of days he began to stand sentry for Joseph's fasting. He would find Joseph lingering by an ash tray with a good-sized butt in it . . . and would catch his wrist in a vise . . . and Joseph later thanked him. One night in despair he absolutely compelled Harry to give him a cigarette to smoke. But when he had it in his mouth with a match going up to it, he simply could not make match and cigarette meet. Then quietly he put the cigarette in his pocket. "I want to keep this. It stabbed me. I want to remember I *could* let myself be stabbed. What's the use of looking at ash trays? I'll keep this to smoke; no halfway business. But I think I'm beating the game. Half the month's gone."

This was beginning to grow to be history, in a life full of cravings and notions, always, indulged.

Here's the last bit we could find on it; it is dated Saturday, Oct. 18—"Tired from nerve-end to end; but full of a sense of strength, which doesn't seem to jibe, and which of course jibes perfectly; it's strength like a wall—not like a brick-and-mortar-wall, nothing like a wall at all, yet a wall—and it's all that keeps back a fire that rolls up to there and . . . can't get over. It's holding the line! Is this what will is? I can't tell, I never had any. But how frail a will-wall is, how materially nothing! Yet the rolling fire that wants to sweep me through from stem to stern of a torpor that wants it to or at least doesn't care if it sweeps or not, can't roar over the wall. And suddenly I want to plunge up that parapet and . . . cheer. And am too aware of my real weakness to. It's only a fragile wall. But not will. It must be that last wall, by which we know something good in us is making a last stand . . . blackened and raked through, tired and nerve-taut, holding the line, a wall, holding the fire, to outlive it or crumble right there. . . . It's the twenty-second day but . . . I don't believe it."

And here's one final note we just find, overlooked because it has no date and didn't seem part of that diary; but it must be:

"I've made an odd discovery, don't know what else to call it: the last point of unbearability *moves.* It moves forward slowly; you find yourself bearing the unbearable; somehow the last roar of flame crackling your final agony to heaven was not the last; suddenly it falls back and you are pushing forward on it; suddenly it has a point like a sword and you push forward on it; it breaks the skin and slides between flesh but still you push forward—and it falls back, the point of last unbearability falls steadily back as you steadily advance. I wonder, wonder, if there is any unbearability; you push forward till the hilt presses the breast and still you would push forward, by some power beyond you drawn past pain? It will be interesting to find out if something's *carrying* me."

He wanted God and couldn't bear to fail in the test. That was obviously all.

He went the whole month. Toward the end it was almost easy. An eagerness not unlike anticipation swept him forward.

He wrote to say he was coming for the profession of faith, "having found I can give up some small part of me for your cause."

Father X was waiting in the beautiful Spanish-mission stone pile, at dusk. He was in a white lace-covered Roman robe with pink breast and back shields, now but hazily remembered. It was very dark in the church. He gave his hand to Joseph for a quick hard grasp. "God bless the effort," he said. "I was worried."

He brought Joseph through the cloistered dusk down to the altar rail, in the dark of which Joseph was bidden to kneel, well down to the right near the cross. The tall dim white robe of the priest went around and he came opposite Joseph to kneel across the rail before him. A great quietness trembled through Joseph in the dark; he felt the more the blessed nearness of the White-robe that had come to the desert to deliver him. The priest struck a match; the flare startled Joseph kneeling at the rail. It flickered a grisly yellow light across the pallor of the priest kneeling before him; then the match sputtered over a candle, whose spark grew, shook, shrugged up and steadied, casting dim light down the gleaming rail along the kneeling-stone. He saw the vague kneeling form of a young woman farther down the rail, and was troubled. "It's all right; we've always had a witness to the taking of the oath; she'll not know who's joining Jesus."

Something lodged in his throat. He was joining the band, for Christ; Him crucified; come what may. The White-robes. This was the last crusade.

He saw a great book open on the rail-top, over a little end-table placed there, all alive in candle quivers. The Bible.

A smaller book was laid open before him. Across the candle light shed by the taper on the book, the white face of the priest wavered in the flickers. "Read it, slowly, just loud enough for me to hear. The other witness is God."

The sentry's oath—

Joseph read slowly, all of him was moved there in that bit of candle light on the rail, where he knelt to profess himself enlisted for—the Carpenter. His voice wavered . . . then went steadily on. It was all right. All life long he had waited for this—waited to swing for the beautiful and true. He was a sword-hand now. At last, Galahad.

He was swearing to defend the kingdom against all its enemies whatsoever, guarding most of all against self. He had joined the army again. But, in this, the fight would end only when death should relieve him. That went through and through. And the hardest fight would be against himself . . . against temptations, darknesses, urges, cravings—flesh, made synonymous with invisible adversaries whom he very well understood, for they had swarmed over his back, over and over. The fight he was proposing against them made him tremble. . . . He was also promising to stand by Christ-on-earth, the Holy Catholic Church; he believed this to be the Church of Jesus Christ, which would be persecuted for His sake; he swore to detest her enemies for His sake: the false witnesses, the defections, the fallen-away branches, the sects grown apart, the heresies of every kind whatever that had forsaken His Church—.

He stopped dead-short. He must swear to hate all the peoples not Christian, and all the people professing Christ in seceding parts of the Church. A beautiful peace had come to him, through this Church, from the Carpenter who gave us God from the cross. It seemed not to agree, somewhere, and it greatly disturbed him, as nothing had ever disturbed him before. All the hard-won new world shook, his one great effort was trembling for a crash . . . and he wanted it not to, not to!

"Do you mind," he said, bursting to be calm, across the candle on the rail beyond which the priest quietly waited, "if I read this last part again? I want to get every part of it in front of me—whole."

"No, read it again; I want you to be absolutely sure."

He read it over, slowly, reviewing the meaning with all the honesty he could command. Then he put his hand on the Bible and took the oath. The priest earnestly prayed for one more sentry . . . who, in the dusk outside, stopped.

"I wanted you to understand what happened. When I stopped suddenly, I couldn't take oath to hate pagans, atheists, Jews, Buddhists, and Protestants—hate people. My whole world shook. I couldn't see Jesus in that. I had to go back, I felt He couldn't have let such a hate get into His Church. Then reading again I found I was asked to hate paganism, atheism, false teachings, splits—desertion and division in any form—whatever rejects or mutilates the institution of Jesus. He asks me to hate anything that cuts His sheepfold up, because it cuts God up and sets man against man—exactly the thing I've hated all my life. So I took the oath."

"You've answered more for yourself by yourself," quietly said the priest, "than if I'd have given you some lessons on it. That's exactly the teaching of the Catholic Church."

In the study the two discussed Joseph's opening life as a practicing Catholic. He could not take Sacraments, because he could not be absolved. He could not be absolved of sins of the past and restored in the state of God's grace—which simply means eligibility for reunion with God if one dies in that state—because he was at the moment living in a state of marriage enacted in disobedience of the Church: for, baptized a Catholic as his wife had been, the two had *disobeyed* the authority to which baptism had bound them as Catholics; they had been married not in the prescribed Sacramental order. In the eyes of God Who has instituted two means of redemption, in the Church and her Sacraments, Joseph was not married at all. He was living in a state of sin.

All this he had quietly learned before, during the lessons on commandments, authority and Sacraments. But now that he had professed his Christian faith in the instituted Church, he found himself barred to the Sacraments. Having long ago accepted the authority of the Church as Christ's mother administering His Sacraments, there was no question about putting himself absolutely under the law of her whom he loved for Mother. Having accepted with all free-will a Jesus as invisible head of the Church instituted by Himself, he had accepted the whole deposit of faith and authority, with all the law, as emanating from Him or by His consent; for He had promised to stand by. Therefore when he found that the priest was without authority to admit him to the Sacraments for which the Church was given to man, because of the bar of unsanctioned marriage, he felt the barrier grievously.

God had instituted the Sacrament of marriage, and he had

ignored it. This must be remedied. For although the two Catholic-born partners had lived in unconscious disobedience, the union was no less an occasion of sin now that the offense against authority was revealed . . . a subject too painful to cast before a wife already made to bear enough through him.

She had flashed at the Catholic teaching that stood suddenly before him. "Then I'm a harlot?— They'll catch me setting foot in that Church again—." Here was a sore in the newest sentry.

But the month of the pain of the cigarette trial had done something. She could see him suffering. She had urged him to end the burning . . . then seeing the effort to bear it she had tried to help him fight. For she saw a man of small persistence suddenly forcing himself to prove his capacity to suffer.

And after her flash at the rule of the mother, the Church, she had said, "Please let me alone; let me think this over for myself."

They sat reviewing this in the priest-house study.

Father X said, "Let it rest. You have done what can be done. Only time and God's grace can do anything, now."

Presently he went on, "Above all, don't intrude at home. Set a quiet good example,—and pray. She already gave the two children; I'm sure she'll let the boy be baptized. . . . If nothing else can be done, we'll see about a dispensation, admitting you."

"Absolutely not," said Joseph. "We come together or not at all. I caused the tangle and I'll swallow being an outsider, an ally." Being an ally of God was better than nothing.

And at home she said that she would see the priest for a clear picture of it all. "But no promises. Leave me alone."

Warmth swept him. . . . They saw the priest together. He explained the case simply. She said she would consider.

An odd thing happened after the profession of faith.

Joseph was stuffing the day's papers and field book into his briefcase, at Relief Headquarters, when he saw Jim the realtor standing apart, smoking.

Joseph went beside the fellow-agent who had attacked the faith so . . . startling the sharp-cut profile. "Jim, the other day in the dark of the church over a candle, I made my profession of faith. When the last bar is let down, if ever," Joseph quietly said, "I hope to become a Catholic." He paused; a quickened gleam had sunk behind the steady gaze. "I thought you might want to know that," Joseph told him.

He went back to pack his bag. The small platoon of ex-soldiers had strung out to various parts of the relief line; the two were alone. He found Jim beside him. The realtor was quiet. "Just why did you think that should interest me?"

"I don't know, Jim," Joseph frankly answered—"unless it's that when I like a man I go by first or instinctive impressions. And I felt in you a calm and a true man. That's why I couldn't understand you overthrowing the Catholic Church in me, that you had caused me to stop attacking; I just couldn't believe you had done that. Yet there was the fact, and it troubled me." He added, "I went through anyhow. You gave me the start. I suppose I wanted you to know that."

There fell silence. Then to Joseph's surprise Jim said,

slowly, "I'm a Catholic. And, in my own small way, I hope I'm a good one. . . . I'm going to hurt you," he went on, simply, "without intending to: I saw you taking up the Catholic Church to examine it, when you had ripped at every man's effort to serve God. To me the Catholic faith is a precious and beautiful thing; I couldn't see you picking it up to examine it, like damaged goods exposed to every fog-mind that comes along; I tried to throw an obstacle across your path, to protect it by forcing you to examine the depth of your intention. I congratulate you."

Joseph found himself flying with this in great gladness to the purser. For now he knew that he had been very fond of the agent.

But the priest grunted, "I still don't see where that was necessary. He might have smashed the faith in you."

"But he smashed the fog," cheerfully said Joseph, "and forced me to know *reasons* why God wasn't another delusion."

Eve grew steadily more ill, though, and one day quickly called Joseph, in swooning pain.

The doctor sent her to the hospital, fearful for her tiredness. They found a confusion of symptoms. There were consultations, out of which they sent for Joseph. "At least two operations seem necessary, major ones; there are really three troubles, all involved and pressing and any one of them serious. It doesn't seem possible that she could come through any one of them." Her internal system was chaos.

She lay there two weeks without change. She wanted to be taken away. Joseph, at her quiet word, assumed responsibility and took her home . . . but soon he had to take her away again, this time going to another hospital. But the same report was made, a complication of operations. They feared starting. They held various consultations with visiting surgeons, for her case roused attention. She drove them away at last in utter weariness, bursting out, "I can tell you more about myself than you'll ever find out all put together; you're all groping." She was there some time, and was extremely patient, would not ask for anything if in asking she might harass the nurse in the undermanned ward. At other times her dry wit kept both patients and staff in laughter . . . which she seemed to time with the discouragement of some other broken woman who was finding herself a burden. But at times too she said wearily that she was enduring more than she could stand, and begged, "Hit me with something, end the pain." The house surgeon and internes were her particular targets. "Think you'll ever learn what's wrong with me?" Or, "Take your claws out of that box; my hubby probably had to steal that candy." They would sit on her bed and eat it the more. "Loosen up: tell us what's wrong with you! You said you could." And when she was in pain she would lift her hands and stonily wave them before her to fight down the moans within. Then they pressed her shoulder. "You're a soldier." The nurse told Joseph all this. Eve was very sensitive about "picking company" . . . and at bottom was the universal man. A woman of refinement was placed beside her because Eve's pluck and jokes seemed medicine; so the nurse took the opportunity to remove the Negro woman whom she had had to put there in an overflow, and put the injured woman there. But in the night Eve's jerky button brought the nurse. "If I have to listen to this chronic kicker I'll scream. The colored one was ten times harder hit and still could try to smile." The nurse moved the woman away, deaf to her threats, and the colored one repaid Eve with a tired smile, beside her again. This was Eve.

But it was tearing her down.

The staff was worried. More consultants crowded the bed; at one time Eve counted sixteen. "I ought to charge admission," she wearily said. They worked all the harder trying to build her up, waiting for time to find the place to start opening and probing.

"I can't last forever," she told Joseph one day, lying there stilled, "I'm afraid this time." It was a knife in him. It scared him. "You were always brought through before," he urged, "when it seemed hopeless." She did not reply.

He had seen the guide that noon before coming to the hospital, and had reported the stalemate over the three conditions. The guide had not commented on that till they were parting; then she had said after a silence: "St. Jude—. I wonder—." This was a cousin of Jesus. For centuries, she said, people had confused the apostle with Judas, so that he was the forgotten apostle, to many unknown. But remarkable answers to prayers made to him had seemed to have been noted recently; a great devotion to the apostle was spreading. "The patron saint of despaired-of cases. Jesus must have done this to restore him to mind among the apostles. Try him." And in the same moment he had silently given the case of his wife to St. Jude, adding within himself, "If you say so in His name, forgotten apostle, I'm sure Jesus will get her up." He mentioned this to his wife as he was about to leave the hospital. But from her stillness she said, "It's more than prayers I need now; it's release—from pain."

She was full of news and humor two days later. She suffered less, she had been entertained. "Another round-up of quacks buzzed over me," she related, in broken breathing, "had a circus." One among them was said to be noted; he was a consultant, come to see the difficult case; after a long probe he asked the staff to show him where the growths and bumps were. They began to show him and he said they must have examined someone else, whereat hot words were spoken. He said he didn't believe there had been anything at any time, "and the interne—the nice one who kids me along—wanted to punch him in the face for insinuating the house surgeons were liars. It was a circus," she chuckled, "I'm getting some fun out of all these tours."

Joseph couldn't understand this; he asked over and over, and she repeated they didn't seem to find anything there. "But they were all worried about all those things in you," he burst. She said nobody knew "anything about anything around here." A few days later she demanded release. "I'm tired of talking to my children through the window; they're not doing anything for me here." The nurse said she would ask. She came back and said she could go on her own responsibility.

She came home. Four months later a doctor massaged her three times and loosened a drawn inner-region.

Gilbert progressed rapidly in the special instructions given by young Father Z. In the winter, Winnie, irrepressible friend of the family, came down with her rapid-fire rumors, dryness and laughs; the family all grouped round the font and Gil was baptized Stephen, after the instructing priest and after the first young man of the Jews to be stoned to death for urging Israel to follow the God-of-the-cross. Winnie and her friend Howard are the godparents.

About that time, the guide asked Joseph if he cared to see what a wedding according to the Sacrament was like. As this question ever pressed on him, he was at once interested. For the guide never suggested a thing that did not have a reason back of it. "Saturday morning at ten," the secretary said. "Be sure to sit a decent distance away from the wedding party;—it's perfectly all right, no intrusion; strangers are never strangers in the Catholic Church, we're all a family, dropping in to pray, and we slip in a prayer for whatever group happens to be gathered in there for something."

Here is the paper we dug up:

"At ten I walked round the garden path, so as to enter from the front, to avoid the intrusion of walking in through a service. Coming in on them from the front, you really walk in on them from behind. Then if you burst in on something, you can drop in a pew right where you are, and not be in the way. Through the side door I blundered in on a nuns' service once, right before their faces, and a children's service another time, and across a whole concourse of kneeling priests in streetwear and cassocks, all mixed, another time. For the church is ever open, every day till late at night; and anything may be going on in there, that a convert knows nothing about, till it's too late to run.

"I found the church dim and shot through with criss-crossed shadow-light; it was drizzling outside, and dark. I went well forward, and sat to the left of the altar aisle, seeing my wedding party clustered to the right front. But they were quite inconspicuously dressed, and sober. I had thought to find a Catholic wedding-in-Jesus a gay affair, because of the joy of the wine of Cana. But my attention all went to the music that came over me as I sat there, low and beautiful and soft, with the pulse of the organ throbbing in it.

"The gentle stream of it soon carried me adrift into a sea of peace . . . from which I started. Altar lights were aglow; four altar boys flitted in by twos across the glow; they were followed in the swell of the organ by priests in black-and-white robes. The music throbbed down; we all stood.

"The music drew a vision before me. Mass was going on. We were kneeling to assist in it. The vision grew and grew. The Episcopalian was marrying the Luna girl to me, a Catholic girl whose ring wouldn't go on; I saw myself pushing and pushing frantically to get the ring on, for the murmur of the minister had stopped. 'I pray God it come off as hard.' Then to the minister's surprise she flashed at him there, 'So, I'm not married?—so, we're just living together; I'm a harlot! You'll catch me setting foot in that Church again!' But she was tired; she was asking my sister about it. 'It's left to me to decide—a ceremony with the Sacrament, at the altar. I don't know if I should or not.' Maybe she would change her mind, it was an immaculately beautiful white altar, glowing too clear for anything but purity to come before it. Robed figures kept flitting before it, blurredly adrift; the pastor was going to the Book. I'd forgotten Mass was here. I abruptly offered up a prayer for the couple of the Nuptial. 'Mother Mary, please ask Jesus to be at the wedding of these two; help him avoid leading his bride through the ditch.'

"And slipping my rosary beads out, I offered the Bouquet of the Roses, having nothing to give the bride. I wondered which among the cluster across the aisle kneeling there could be the bride.

"The music grew again, it began to live. It had pulse. It was soft life; somehow not gay life, it didn't lilt; it had no dance to it, but something better—something fragile and yet peacefully strong, with a timbre of steadiness in it, that was suddenly twilight, peace, a place to come home and lie down and let rest come. Home-after-work. Something in it seemed Adam, staggering down among the boulders, bearing us all on his back, children of his exile; and somehow I felt the unbearable aloneness—all generations accusing the father, who burst into tears. '*I* didn't mean it,—it looked all right—.' And down among the rocks he stumbled under his Albatross, a backful of children, his sobs gone stilled, like a memory of darkness that had sobbed and murmured away. I came jolting back. Somewhere across my mind had trodden a far beat, steadily nearing with muffled sound; a shadow flitted slowly across the corner of my eye, another—a slow parade—.

"I stood kneeling quite still. For, coming into the aisle upon a sorrowing throb of music, were men, bearing a large gray casket—. Here came the bride. The groom was death.

"Lord, what an ignorant man this is. I didn't know a dirge from a wedding march.

"But I offered this prayer: 'God, I didn't know anything. Keep that prayer for the bride, all the same. May it shorten her way home to You, a bit.'"

Discouragement began to set in. Trying to practice Christianity, he was discharged from relief.

Seeing his hundred families tired and friendless, he felt moved; for a Thanksgiving present, the Bureau notified them that no rents could be paid this month, and food in less quantity. To help the spirit brighten a bit, he organized the community for a Cheer-up Party, which the people quickly supported; the chain grocers sent food, the little storekeepers filled in, music was to come, and acts of entertainment. There was to be for the families on relief a night of food, dancing and vaudeville, all contributed by the people.

But the Social Service doctors sent for Joseph and accused him of stupidity. "You're reminding them that they're indigent," they said. "Then, damn-it-to-hell," burst Joseph, "why remind them that they're slaves, cutting out their rent and giving less food, for Thanksgiving? I cheer up indigents; you cut them down and go eat your stuffed turkey." He was swiftly sent packing. His Bureau Chief burned the telephone wires wearily all afternoon, to get him reinstated. But Joseph never knew he had been discharged till days after. "Put a padlock on your heart," grunted the Chief; "you're in Social Service now. Everything is scientific; you have to learn to starve them with psychology."

He was beginning to feel a battle within himself. The spiritual became translated more and more into terms of everyday efforts to make himself over, that was why. There *is* a Pilgrim's Progress and in Joseph it was ragged. He would gain a step and go down on his back for a loss of six; and it would be weeks before he would find the calm again.

Somehow he had begun to write filth again, in spasmodic

starts that were not at once attacked by the sentry in him; he seemed not there. It stunned Joseph; he felt he had rolled down the whole path to the ditch.

In reality, a serious reaction took place. He could not face the altar. He hovered within the desert again; he did not find it honest to lift himself to God any more.

A little crumpled pile of foul writing had caused this stillness. How much of this had been discouragement over the schism at home, cannot be definite. But probably it was self, merely self. It is in every pilgrim.

There followed several broken nights of sleep . . . and a nightmare . . . from which he jumped to find the pillow stuffed in his throat to still a cry of terror, as in childhood when ghosts had flitted.

The bedroom was pitch dark. He could not get rid of the idea that an evil presence filled the dark even when he jerked the light on. He tried to sleep it off as nerves; but a nightmare worse than the first brought his wife hurrying in, for he had cried out.

She found him on his knees, babbling a prayer with his rosary beads wound round his hands. "It's all right," he wearily said, "there won't be another nightmare." Tired, he put the beads under his pillow, then crushed them in his hand, and fell into a quiet sleep . . . waking up to find his hand still clutching the beads . . . or the hand of Mother Mary, to whom he must have fled again.

That night he went to walk the stations of the cross. He found people sitting sparsely around in the dark, a single candle lighting the altar, and many candles glowing at the rack for Joseph-and-Jesus and the rack for Mary, down front; it was Saturday night . . . confession night. Along the walls, two lines were shuffling up slowly to the boxes in which men bare their burden, accusing themselves; tomorrow was Mass, and Bread for the penitents of the night. He could not receive this, for he was but an ally. Down the wall he went and around, wearily praying at each station of the cross in the dark. Twice he stood hovering on the verge of walking out with his soiled hands; the third time he turned and did walk out into the night, but a great unwillingness stopped him on the lawn. "Mother, guide me," he begged the mother of the beads . . . and was going down the other wall again.

In the dark he stood by a station, where they were stripping Jesus. He could not look at the dim creaminess on the tablet in the dark; he felt too foul to continue. There was a shabby woman kneeling in the dark pew beside him, he could feel her dim face suddenly on him, and grew aware he was a public spectacle. Across the humiliation came a flash of Rome, and of the faithful burdened with sin waiting by some Christian place, to beg fellow-Christians to remember them in their prayers. It all seemed so far, so childish, and he stood there at the station, shuffling uneasily, digging at his eyes with knuckles.

Then turning around he begged the woman, "Pray for me!" And was embarrassed by a rush of tears.

The woman said, "I certainly will." There was a small girl kneeling on the other side of her and to her she said, "Go to the cross for the man, pray God to help him." The little girl rose up and went down in the dark, appeared again across the candle-rack glow and could be seen kneeling under the cross on the wall, hands clasped to her chin, her profile lifted to the Carpenter outstretched.

Joseph was struck with this, and with his own abrupt plea that had moved it. He said amazedly to himself, "Look, a little girl on her knees prays for me." He did not understand these far-world things that were suddenly so near. But a warmth came through the blur and it was not uneasiness. He recognized the tiredness, even the childishness. But it had peace behind it.

And at the altar rail he quietly thanked God and the Maiden of Israel who caused it all.

He had prayed in the beginning for belief to come, praying to a window shade. Then when God began to dwell in his whole consciousness, he never knew whether it was really conversion; he could *see,* but who can convince himself that the consciousness is faith? He saw still the same man full of himself, trying to *feel* Christian. He hated pretense. He was afraid he merely longed to believe; he could recognize no honest penance in himself, no sorrow to give God, no love. He did try to see life through a Creator, and could try to make his life over to be as Forgiveness would have us; he was aware of this. But it was his performance that discouraged him. In which, perhaps, he is like his neighbor.

With his small faith, not even sure that there was a Godhood there to listen, he now began to petition all heaven for his wife's conversion. It became a real siege of petitions. He feared only that she would be shut out forever from the garden.

The burden of his petitions was that she had not disobeyed

God but that she had followed her man; he would even find himself commending her to God for the great constancy with which she followed;—he hastened to plead that she had gathered only sorrow as the reward for following such a leader, with a prayer in her heart to Him for them all, every foot of the way. "She made my way her way, my bread her bread, my sickness her sickness, Lord," he would urge, "only to find that coming behind me, she has gone the other way." And pleading that it be charged to his account, he would recall to Him that she had sent her two children back to Him. And he besieged all the saints with the same prayer, asking them to intercede for them both.

He made this petition in all his Masses, all his morning and evening prayers; then during the day he searched for new saints to make novenas to, offering roses to the Rosary Queen, and he walked the stations of the cross for this cause, with his mind ever open for ways to enlist additional intercession, till in all his consciousness there seemed room for little else.

At last he began to send up this petition only to the saints and the Blessed Mother, because he found it more and more hard to appeal to the Deity—especially the Weariness-on-the-cross. For he felt the Carpenter quietly saying, more and more, "I sent the Luna girl to you; where is the Galahad I sent her to?"

Until one day under the rush of all he was trying to undo as he lingered down a wall of the stations, he begged to be delivered of the whole burden, it was unbearable. And again begged to retain it. Then he realized the months' strain had unstrung him.

The guide came, and said the Mission was come to the parish. This week it was for the women, whether believers or not; next week the men were to go. Through missionaries of the cross, the Apostles were to speak again, to the man-in-the-street. "I wonder if you'd care to go. I've a feeling you should," she said. He was very tired, but he went. For there was always a good result coming after the doing of what this guide put before him.

Here is a final paper recording the Mission and the outcome that swept over a family, like a storm breaking full upon them:

"Tomorrow the Mission ends. We are seven hundred men jammed in a Catholic church, drawn from nobody knows where. Some are skeptics, come to review; others are representatives of scattered beliefs, by some power gathered here among these Catholics, who came to hear again about their faith, and learn how far they have wandered from it. Perhaps a third are on Home Relief or one door from it; some shirk employment; a few certainly have been more at home in dives. Here are men as they come in from the night: the banker and the drifter, the artist and the soldier, the local merchant and his servant, the man from Wall Street and the man from a saloon, a ship, a jail, a sick-bed, anywhere. Nowhere does it seem possible to gather such a universal man. But when I see us here, where the six hundred Judiths, Jezebels, Magdalenes and Lot's wife sat last week, I begin to visualize what Judgment Day should look like. Here we are, the multitude that came to stone the woman, and that crept away one by one in man's seeing of himself.

"I saw a withered old man dragging himself in, hand-over-hand along the kneeling rail, behind a youth with all life wondering in his gaze; and down in the pews, in spotless neatness, a Negro, sitting in his aloneness within a multitude. And farther across, alert-eyed and wrinkled, a Chinese dried out in some laundry. Yet it was not the contrasts, it was the great number of settled men, family heads, that struck me—men who are in the full swing of trying to get their families through life, burning and recasting and burning again, going on somehow;—and looking at the anonymity, I thought I caught the calm face of the man-in-the-street, with the blows of life healing under the eyes, Adam's son, taking a moment's rest from his weary wondering what it's all about. And to me that seemed dignity.

"They have been streaming in for some time, quickly filling the church, or kneeling in droves down the long rail, before the altar, before the images of St. Anthony, Joseph, The Little Flower, and Our Lady of Try-again . . . and the Cross, where a man is putting his derby down and topcoat over the rail, kneeling to touch his finger to the nailed feet a moment, while the overcoat slides off into the court, and a wanderer trips over his feet behind. Somehow here is life, coming to ask if *this* is what it's all about. Everywhere I see them, young and graying and old, strong and feeble, burlesque-goer and church-goer, streaming into the pews, while down the walls in endless uneven procession, droves follow the way of the cross, some fast, some lingering, and others making it a ritual indeed.

"Then suddenly one of the two black-robes with the heart on the breast and the cross thrust into the waist-rope, comes in bearing a tall wooden cross, which he plants on the platform in the altar court while everywhere men go to find seats. Then without preliminary, under the towering cross, facing us, he makes the sign of the cross, saying in unison with us, 'In the name of the Father, the Son and the Holy Ghost; Amen.' And another night of the Mission is on, opened with the united saying of the rosary.

"I sit stilled tonight, because today all the past rose up and stood before me, like a shower of fists in the face, till I could hardly stand it and yet must. I had sought out one of the two apostles the third day, moved as I had been moved on Good Friday; and, asking for Father Cletus of the quiet word and lashing after-effect, again a feeling of seared nerves behind a mission calm made me think of truth seeking a listener in the street. And I felt myself muddying it.

"Who will describe a monk of the cross? His day is spent planting the cross in the street; few men can serve like this. The strain is exactly that of the battle-field; it never ends; they smash in the middle of it, these men of the clear-piercing intelligence, that could draw a fortune out of Wall Street. All this strain is for bread and board; and in a pogrom they are the first killed.

"Therefore when they talk they consider only the message handed down to them, and it rips the mask off where it finds it. Then it preaches Christ crucified, as Paul did.

"Into Father Mac's study came this quiet man who *looked* gray, yet who was not old. It was that he suggested a wall that has been battered, overswept, burned, mined . . . and will stand. There seemed something behind that, that would level walls before it of its own power. Here was youth spent in universities, then cut down in ten years of hard learning in search of men's theories and systems, where the intellect must ferret out wheat from chaff; they come out burned out, many of them, and the rest pass on to the searchlight of teachers trusted with the cross . . . who throw out all but the knife-like mind that can first of all accept its absolute reasons for faith, and then cut through everything behind which fellow-intellects in the world may argue the myth of the cross, and every sham put up by men professing to be worthy of its redemption. For they are to pass it on, its message.

"I stood suddenly before a sentry of the cross.

"And to him I told my whole case, which, passing back through this penetrating intellect, came rising before me so suddenly as the picture of myself, that I could not bear it.

"He made me see a creature, confused, illogical, badly mis-educated with a smattering of surface gleanings, and all shot through with self; he even ignored the thing I had done when I had thought to challenge a Deity, and ignored the attacker of belief in anything higher than self. My account of it soon floundered and stopped. He was cold, calm, absolutely impersonal with us both, and cut me down without sparing a feeling.

"'You call yourself an atheist, but have no system of thought. I can't argue with you; what must I oppose? Your self? What is more beneath contempt! As I sat here listening to you setting that up, with a life confused beyond study, I grew actually sick. You're hardly an enemy—except in the arrogant self-appraisal of your power to damage. An analysis of you can be made in the few minutes of sitting here: you're a remarkable example of what is known as a choked-up mind; you've found a bad general education without any depth or direction at all, plus a scattered amount of reading—bits of philosophy and authors, good and bad and most unwisely picked, never anyone's system of thought followed through to its conclusion as the basis on which to test your own thought; and you're stuffed with it, it's not assimilated, your mental life is clogged, stunned. I heard you mention education. Don't ever call yourself an educated man.'

"I could have gone through the floor.

"He went on, curtly, 'Your kind clogs the world. Without a message, you leave high school and college and go out through a scattering of books, to shout about the emancipated self you have found; and you call that freeing the mind! You're less poison than rot, spread out over your little area, bothering the taxpayers who paid to lead your mind out to fit it into the world and make it better, smearing your foulness over every newspaper and magazine and book that will stoop to print your ton of words about it.'

"'We have to enlighten the world with the great mind we trained,' I said, and began to cry, as I knew damned well I soon must. 'My father didn't send me out to do this; it'd turn him sicker than you can suppose, seeing his son before you—. That's what hurts. I wanted him to be proud of me; he's an honest man; I've been trying to start over—.' I broke. 'It's a job—.'

"He was troubled about me, I could see that through every word he had said; but he sat absolutely apart from the scene before him, with a coldness all the more penetrating because he must put away himself to get it whole.

"That is exactly what forced me to bear myself when I could not bear it.

"'I hate it as much as you do,' I said, 'I'm not proud of it, it's a knife through me, to see myself.'

"I had stopped crying. 'What you said is all true. It's right on the nose.'

"Then he said, quietly, 'You wrote and acted against Christ and the Church. Try to write for the Church now.'

"He stood up then, the interview was over. He suggested that I go to my priest of the convert course, and report myself. I found him suddenly kindly; and across a simple handclasp I saw that he was really pounded within by the strain of giving the cross in the market-place.

"He urged—and I caught the distant weariness, 'Pray for me now and then.'"

Joseph has tried to remember him in every prayer, and every Mass.

He had intended merely to see a night of the Mission, but he remained throughout the seven days. He had never heard straight talk like this, that hit across a silence in which one false note struck by the missioner must have raised a murmur of growls in this mixed difficult crowd. There was humor, too. These black-robed men appreciated a laugh in the day's course; they could see the funny side of man even in the field of trying to find God; Father Cletus' partner, especially, brought down laughter in roars, with his reminiscences of converts and the faithful alike, blundering along the pilgrim's path; and now and then the loudest laughter rose up when he was not laughing, but lashing out at some sour trait in us brought out by him so suddenly that the men could see man's absurdity even when it was a blow in the face.

But the words that struck swiftest across that silence were

the short blunt ones that shot out in that uncompromising truth which no man will take except from his own father . . . and from a Passionist. It was here that the mask was jerked off worship to expose a lie: "I've got more respect—and you may as well have it to your face—for one open atheist who lets the world know just where he stands, than for a churchful of hypocrites," and how the word cracked forth! "whose life is a lie to the Catholic Church, whose bad example is a dagger in her back;—a-ah, you're not fooling anyone—the priest may take your faked confession—but it had been better had that hypocrite never been born, for the score of treason and ingratitude that he's chalking up against himself, with his heart shut to charity."

They detested hypocrisy, these missioners, less only than the deliberate renouncing of God, particularly when the apostate has been given the gift of faith in the Catholic Church, which was described as the pearl of great price, the blood of Christ. Here the reality of his desertion struck Joseph, the Catholic-born, and it struck all the more because of the interview of the afternoon. He had not realized how beautiful the thing called the Catholic faith could be, till he spoke with and heard some non-Catholics who seemed unable to enter it because of some barrier of circumstance. And to him this thing had been given at birth, Madonna had made childhood glow. He had sold it for a daub of mud. The words hit him in the face; they were like fists. He was not surprised to find his heart itself stung with tears. He could feel the holy revulsion of the prophet Jeremiah, stinging out through Father Cletus' partner under the cross: "Know then that it is an evil and bitter thing for thee to have left the Lord thy God."

Yet it was quiet, calm Father Cletus, following his partner under the cross, who shook Joseph to the core. There is no cut like the wrath of a peaceful man. He stood there in his indescribable silence, looking for ears to hear. Then quietly he began, "We preach one thing, only. Christ, crucified."

He gave them also themselves. Before them was revealed all the consciousness of a man who sees, in the multitude sitting there, the God they nailed to wood, when they had no intention of nailing a God at all. And now Joseph thought he saw what grayed him, standing there under his cross, as if under a street lamp, seeking an ear to know the *longing* of a God to untangle man from himself. The missioner saw what every clear intelligence devoted to a forgiving Creator must see as the day shortens: the fallacy of throwing a rope to a drowning man who does not want to be drawn out. That it was human *not* to see a rope in the fullness of living, was the thing that was wearing this man down, Joseph felt sure. His quiet talk was exactly that, between the lines. His very earnestness shook. He was speaking not only of people outside, but of men in the pews.

Suddenly the talk was shortening its note, jerking its stride; he had for the moment broken away from the restraint of the start. And as the words shortened, Joseph sat suddenly taut. The attack was on himself; the missioner was hurling the cheaply educated mind's worship of the god Self at the multitude—and it struck Joseph. Father Cletus was nauseated. He gave the multitude all the arrogance of a distorted mind that must imagine itself challenging God, for no other reason than to "express myself" under the stars; and in the stillness across which this revulsion shook, Joseph could feel Catholics and visitors alike finding a universal contempt for that type of superiority, that must loudly order meat on Friday because a man asks for fish. His head went down . . . and lifted itself because this was what he had come for. . . .

He saw the missioner, pausing in a silence, standing there under the cross; it seemed useless. His weary gaze drifted across the multitude. Then without closing his words the black priest bade them kneel, and himself knelt on one knee with hand groping to the cross. His face lifted to it for that mute, beautiful plea, "God-of-the-cross—hear us, help us to save our soul; we are Thine, and Thine we wish to be . . ." the brothers, all drifted apart . . . "help us drift back home again, one by one. . . ."

Through rain or dawn-glow's cold, he walked, mornings, to the Mass of the seven hundred, to hear the word again and see them, line on line, taking the Blessed Sacrament, the regiment of prodigal sons. It choked him. He wanted to be going down to be relieved with that battle-shocked line, to Him, and he must stumble up alone to take the last barricade . . . his wife. He did not know how much longer he could. . . . And at night he walked to the southern town again to hear the message. During the day he prayed for the seven hundred, and for all men, and tried to lift himself to God.

Friday he took a turn on that respite line and entered a box to accuse and unburden himself of all his sins. Then suddenly, "Hold on— Who instructed *you?* You can't come in here, I have no power to absolve you—you're not admitted to all this, you're living in disobedience in that marriage. . . . You shouldn't have come, you know," Father Cletus' partner not unkindly repeated, "you're outside."

His fibres all trembled. You must go to bare yourself unbearably for a clean garment and be pitched naked into the street instead, to appreciate this. Or had the guide sent him for exactly this last humiliation, to abase that self in him?

He had had an impulse to snarl out, "Aw, go to hell, the whole lot of you," and end one more experiment, the last.

Instead, he got up nodding, "O.K.," and stood a minute outside trying to control that trembling rebel, a sob bursting out in the street. All his emotion was just under the skin that day. A tired man's sob is a ghastly thing. He checked it.

He went back next morning the same as before, through the Mission day. For one week he had lived as the early White-robes . . . and had turned the other cheek.

He was rewarded Saturday with unutterable beauty. He stood in total dark with the arrayed regiment of seven hundred—and at least six hundred and fifty of them raised lighted candles with Joseph in the catacombs again, pledging to keep the torch that had been flung to them by Stephen of the Jews. And in the brilliant pinpoint dark, across a guttering sea of steadiness, was it the troubled Tired sire in him renewing for Joseph the baptismal oath?

Or it was Joseph trying to redeem the deserter, Galahad.

Suddenly a Mission came to his village parish. There was an announcement over the Sunday Mass rail, and Joseph took it home. At the Mass he had prayed, one last time, "Please, Lord, bring her to the Mission—I know You'll lift her over the wall if she comes to hear You." And offered his Mass on that.

He told her the Mission was coming a week from now, women's week first, beginning next Sunday night.

"*So* what?"

"I thought you'd want to know."

She said after a silence, "I'll think it over." And murmured, "I'd like to hear a straight word."

Sunday came; but as the time neared, she made no move to dress for it. At last he quieted the trembling and said timidly, "It will soon start, the Mission."

"I'm not going, I don't want to bother."

All his world quivered.

"Why do you look like that at me?" she demanded.

He had a feeling that if she didn't go it was all over.

"I don't know, what can I say? I'm sure if you go you'd see—"

She cut that at once. She made it plain; she was *not* going to be pushed into something simply because *he* wanted it. He said it was for her, he wasn't thinking of himself. Her laugh tore at this. "That's all you ever thought of, yourself. Well, this time I'm following my own mind, that's all. I'm *not* going."

He stood still, then quietly because the crash shook he said, "Then you've taken it out of my hands. I'm bound by the oath I took to stand by Christ. His law is the Church; the Church finds me living in a state of sin, an unsanctioned marriage." He felt the thrust coming. "To save us disobeying, I'm not going to have any more acts of union. There's nothing I can do but obey."

The blood left her face.

"So—the Church means more to you than I do, is that it?"

"I can't answer that—you know that's unfair," he protested; "the Church to me is God—"

"I think," she said in the hung moment, "I have a right to an answer."

He found the last wall. "Honey, you're my world; if it falls I smash with it—but God to me means more than the world and all in it; I don't love you any less; God I put above everything, that's all."

"You've been wanting that Church, above even—" She bit her trembling lip. "All right, keep it; if I'm less—"

She stood swaying, but calm. "I'll pack up tonight. You're free." And forcing back tears she left him there.

The swordthrust—.

But what rocked him was that it had burst not through him but his woman, hilt smashing her breast . . . handle in his hand.

Toward dusk he found her seated on the back porch-step, stilled in loneliness. He lingered there in a separate world; who would bridge it now? "I've brought you nothing but heartache," he tremblingly said, "but it was the one good intention of my life—somehow. I went through conversion to lead you back to the God I took you from."

"I wouldn't follow you any more if it was to heaven,—I've given you all I had, following you," she said, with a quivering mouth, "and got burned;—I could never follow you again." She was crying within, the hardest kind, on the step, with suppressed sobs.

He did not intrude; something told him not to intrude on this, not by word or touch. He made a last silent plea, "Guide us now, St. Joseph—tell me what to do."

She was sitting now in red-eyed silence. Last tears rolled down. With her lip she sucked in a drop that trickled. The aloneness stabbed him. This was the Luna girl.

"Honey," he shakily said, squatting on haunches beside her; "don't jump at me;—for just one minute I want to try to be your friend. Trust me for a minute. I won't lead you astray."

She hesitated, he urged, "Let me say just this: I've had only one thought and that's God for our house to guide us. I know how you felt, thinking I must be cracked, gone fanatic,—but Honey, be kind to me for just this little: call it an experiment again; I honestly saw God and tried to get my bearings;—I know I went astray somewhere, but that's because I've been trying to do the impossible, make myself over—. Wasn't the month without cigarettes, something new? Wasn't all that daily prayer, something new? Could human flesh have resisted that woman who wanted to jump over with me? I sat still; wasn't that something new? I tried to be a Christian, Honey," he pleaded, "because I thought I could see a God at last. And, Eve, I had to stand there and choose between you and the God I tried to see, when the knife sank through us both. Could a man have done that for less than God?"

She sat uncertainly; tears streaked her profile again. He touched her shoulder and said huskily, "Honey, I'm not your enemy, I'm trying to be your friend. It wasn't that I wanted you to attend the Mission, but that I felt God there; and I felt that if you could freely let yourself go, hear the word of two men who haven't got a thing to sell, maybe you might get a picture of what I've been moved by, and understand what I've been trying to do, better, a little."

"I followed you so much before; I trusted you so—"

"I know," gently in his tears. "Don't follow me now. Go and just hear—just get God's side as the Church sees it, then do as you feel right. Look," he urged, "if you go, I'll promise this: that even if it damns me, I'll abide by *your* decision;—if you don't find God in there worth a man's giving up the world and all life for, when you come back I'll—I'll do without the God you couldn't find;—I'll stand by—take whatever destiny suits you— A man can't lose more than that."

He arose and stood there; she was up too, stunned of face. Then touching the back of his hand she said gently as she turned to leave him, "I'll go."